Power of Excellence

1915 - 1990

Allison

Power of Excellence

1915 - 1990

Allison Gas Turbine Division
General Motors Corporation

by
Paul Sonnenburg
and
William A. Schoneberger

Designed by Robaire Ream

Coastline Publishers

Allison
75
1915·1990

The Allison 75th Anniversary Logo Timothy A. Smith, winner of Allison's 1990 logo contest, works at Plant 5 in the Model 250 area as a lathe operator on the computerized Lathe Special Automatic. Smith, a 12-year Allison employee, majored in visual communication at the Herron School of Art in Indianapolis, where he earned his B.F.A. in 1973.

Staff for Allison / Power of Excellence
    Allison Gas Turbine Division
Authors: Paul Sonnenburg and William A. Schoneberger
Research: William C. Campbell, Jack R. Evans, Bruce B. Roberts, Joan Zigmunt
Interviews: William Campbell, Jack Evans, Bruce Roberts, Paul Sonnenburg
Photo Editor: Paul Sonnenburg
Design and Typesetting: Robaire Ream
Production Assistant: Lee Mersini
Printing: Walsworth Publishing Company, Marceline, Missouri

Library of Congress Cataloging in Publication Data
    Sonnenburg, Paul, 1937-
        Allison power of excellence.
        Includes index.
        1. Allison Gas Turbine Division General Motors
    Corporation—History. I Schoneberger, William A. II. Title
    Library of Congress Catalog Card Number: 90-83222
    ISBN 0-9627074-0-6
© 1990 Coastline Publishers, Malibu California. All rights reserved
Printed in the United States of America
by Walsworth Publishing Company, Marceline, Missouri
First Edition

Lockheed's legendary P-38 was conceived in 1937 by Kelly Johnson and Hall Hibbard. Christened Lightning by Britain's Royal Air Force in 1940, the swift and deadly fighter was in continuous action on all fronts throughout World War II. Allison V1710 engines for the more than 10,000 P-38s built in 18 variants ranged from the prototype's 960 hp to 1,600 hp for the P-38L.

CONTENTS

About This Book

In 1988 Blake Wallace requested that a book be written commemorating Allison's 75th Anniversary and asked a team of Allison people to put the project together.

The undertaking proved to be much easier said than done. The most significant challenge was selecting the material. That from the files, plus that which was contributed by many people, was, in a word, voluminous.

The two authors, Bill Schoneberger and Paul Sonnenburg, are both products of the aviation industry. Readers of other aviation books and corporate histories of companies such as ours will see the authors' names repeated. They write with an intriguing, flowing style that will have you reading on.

Of course, that is what we were after, a book about Allison that would be interesting to employees present, past, and future.

As mentioned before, the material was overwhelming, just for one book covering 75 years. We had to choose. We chose engines, for the most part, and their application to aircraft and industrial uses. Of necessity, this leaves out quite a bit that could possibly be the subject of other books.

Seventy-five years is a long time in this business and to reach such a milestone demonstrates the durability of Allison and its people.

Creating this book was a great learning experience for us and we wish Allison well for another 75.

Bruce Roberts
Bill Campbell

Foreword

Allison's 75-five-year history is a story of speed, power, and technology. But the real story is the people—men and women whose energy and creativity carried Allison through four major wars and produced generations of new products. The present employes at Allison share the spirit and pride of accomplishment that our predecessors must have known, and feel a responsibility to continue that tradition of excellence.

When World War I descended upon us, Jim Allison's instructions were: "Take the tough jobs, take the jobs that others can't do." Allison people did them, in some cases with breathtaking speed and innovation.

That's what I found at Allison when I came in 1983: an organization that was capable of rising to the challenge. In these past few years, with renewed investment and support from GM, the dedicated effort of the entire team has placed Allison in a strong position to enter the next 75 years. Modern facilities; new products; good positioning of turboprop, light industrial, and helicopter engines; entry into the booming regional airline market; and advanced technology for energy and military leadership all bode well for continuing the Allison tradition.

F. Blake Wallace

General Manager

Allison Gas Turbine Division

Vice President

General Motors Corporation

ACKNOWLEDGEMENTS

Researching, interviewing and assembling source material and photos for a document of this magnitude covering the entire spectrum of Allison's 75-year history is a massive undertaking. It requires a team of dedicated people willing not only to share their memories and memorabilia but also to pitch in to do a lot of "thankless" digging. It is impossible for us to single out one group or an individual for services "over and above" since each of those listed has made contributions to bring this history book to fruition. So, much as it is a challenge to read, we have listed alphabetically — as a way of evidencing our thanks — each individual who contributed time and information for this book.

We hope you will show it to your family, to your children, to your grandchildren and, yes, even to your great grandchildren.

Our special thanks go to the Indianapolis Motor Speedway photo department and the Indiana University Department of Oral History, Bloomington.

But, we reserve a particularly warm "thank you" for:

Larry Allman, Earl Anderson, Wally Anderson, John Arvin, Dick Askren, Scott Baier, Andy Bailey, Jack Bailey, Bryce Baldwin, Jeanette Baldwin, Paul Bancel, Larry Banks, Ray Bannister, Gene Barc, Hill Barrett, Dan Basehore, John Beetham, John Bergman, Donald Beringer, O.H. Billman, Tom Brandenberg, Gus Broffitt, Ed Brunes, James Burris, Mel Byers, Marilyn Campbell, Derrell Cannon, John Cartwright, Hubert Cheesman, Diana Chenoweth, Tom Ciskowski, Dave Cody, Dick Coffey, Bill Compton, John Conti, Bob Cook, Morris Crane, Leo Cuffari, John Custer, Ross Cutler.

Len Davidson, Don Davis, Louis Deck, Bob DePree, Walt DeRoo, Jim Dietz, Sue Dodds, Dennis Duke, Add Dunn, John Dunn, Dick Duzan, Ken Dye, Norm Eggers, W. G. Emmick, Jack Evans, Carol Federspill, Dave Fenwick, Dick Fisher, Jerry Flanders, John Follmer, Don Frankel, Ray Frees, Ken Frost, Gary Fuquay, Dick Gillum, John Goldthwaite, Dick Goodin, R. Green, D.C. Grey, Dennis Grey, Ralph Hart, Bob Hatch, Ted Hawes, John Hayden, William Heady, Harry Helbig, Gene Helms, Gary Hentrup, Joe Hester, Bob Hicks, Ward Hinds, Frank Hintze, Mrs. Gordon Holbrook, Jim Holman, Roger Hooker, Bob Hoover, Chuck Hoover, Michael Horton, Dick Hoyt, Mike Hudson, Bill Hutson, Regina Jackson, Dan Jacobsen, John Jacox, Harlan Jobes, Herb Karsch,

Tony Kennington, Bob Keough, John Kirkpatrick, John Kistler, Johnny Kline, Jim Knott, Henry Korte, Eric Krueger, Dick Kurzawa, Jack Kurzawa.

Steve LaMotte, Bud Lander, John Latcovich, Harold Leahy, Ruby Lester, John Lingeman, Whitey Lingeman, Tim Long, Howard Lord, Frank Losonsky, Jay Lotz, Bob Lowry, Jim Lunsford, Ernie Mackey, Jr., Phil Malone, Manners, W. Maple, Albert Maxwell, Jim Mayfield, George Mayo, Gloria McCallister, John McCardle, Wayne McIntire, Dick McKenna, Denise McNamara, Carl McNeely, Fritz Medenwald, Nick Meko, Barry Miller, Betty Miller, Jack Mitchell, Larry Mitchell, Don Moench, Al Morjig, Donald Morrison, Dean Mosser, Roger Mosser, Buzz Neate, John Newkirk, Jerry Niemann, Kurt Niemann, Stan Nelson, Dave Newill, Dan Nigro, Al Novick.

Dave Oeth, Don Orme, Bob Owens, Phil Painter, Lois Paul, Richard Paul, George Pederson, Tony Perona, Clarence Perry, Sid Perry, Carl Pieper, Richard Pierson, Dave Power, Dave Quick, Diane Raflo, Steve Rainey, Marv Recht, Bob Reed, J.R. Reed, Katherine Reed, Bill Richardson, Wayne Ricks, Ross Rigby, Barb Riggs, Larry Ritter, Mrs. Horace Roberts, C. Rockwood, Xavier Romero, Paul Rose, Bob Roth, Kaye Rush.

Hugh Sample, Paul Sappenfield, Bill Sare, Jim Sauer, Rick Schenkel, Carl Settles, Scott Shadwick, Noble Shepherd, Rex Shields, Ed Sickmeier, John Siegrist, Carolyn Smith, Donald Smith, G. Smith, O.P. Smith, Al Sobey, David South, Bill Sparks, Paul Sparks, Bob Spoon, Bill Springer, Eloy Stevens, R.J. Stewart, Mary Stowers, Dave Sulkoske, Chris Swain, Jon Swanson.

Fred Tangman, Bill Thomas, C.H. Thomas, Angus Thompson, Rob Titlow, Joe Turner, Larry Van Buskirk, Gene VanCleve, Marilyn Vandeventer, Jan Vaughn, Frank Verkamp, Gene Wade, Chuck Wagner, Blake Wallace, Frank Walters, Floyd Waters, Johnny Watson, Harvey Welch, Bob Wente, John Wheatley, John Whitmore, Warren Wilkes, Jim Willeford, Wanda Willis, Lowell Woodard, Joan Zigmunt, Bev Zolezzi.

Bill Campbell, Bruce Roberts
Indianapolis, Indiana
August, 1990

CHAPTER 1
Preparing

James Allison, family, background, and career to 1917; personal qualities, attitude, associates.
Beginnings, development, key people, operation of predecessor companies; Carl Fisher,
P.C. Avery and the Concentrated Acetylene Company; Prest-O-Lite; The Speedway; Indianapolis Speedway Team Company.

Excellence is a word often abused in today's culture and commerce. However, few corporate organizations can be so aptly said to exemplify the word's authentic meaning as the Allison divisions of General Motors. The accomplishments of the men and women of these unique enterprises, from the outset of the Allison companies 75 years ago, endure as proof of their dedication to genuine excellence.

This notion of excellence, the concept of quality and a dedication to doing the job right, are documented in the illustrious history and heritage of Allison that began with one man's devotion to doing worthwhile things superbly.

James Ashbury Allison

Often as significant as a man's measurable accomplishment is his contemporary reputation, particularly for achievers of Jim Allison's stature. Certain Allison characteristics recur consistently in the observations of his friends and colleagues. He was genuinely admired by his business associates. He had an instinct for business opportunity, and the perseverance to support his plans. He worked harmoniously with others. He was regarded as providing the balance and organization for enterprises that sometimes began as dreams. But the success of those enterprises appears directly linked to his aptitude for practical business as well as a capacity for intense concentration on whatever venture claimed his interest. Moreover, a single thread runs through this legend: Jim Allison's passion for quality.

The Allison Family in Indiana

In October 1967 amateur historian John W. Kirkpatrick presented a slide show at a meeting of the GM Regalers Club that he titled "Jim Allison & Friends." From Kirkpatrick's narrative, portions of this introduction to Jim Allison are freely adapted.

The Allison family arrived in Indiana in 1840. Born in England, James M. Allison brought his Scots bride Julia to the Indiana frontier and was soon established in Greene County, say local records, as a Worthington businessman of property who owned a fleet of river boats that plied between Worthington and Louisville, Kentucky. The rivers were then the only highways into an unknown land, linking the first settlements, providing power for mills and industry, and bearing the commerce of goods and ideas.

The couple's son Noah was born in 1846, and when the boy was 12, the family moved to Hillsdale, Michigan. There the father earned local prominence, apparently as a wholesale grocer. Noah was educated in Hillsdale, grew to manhood, and joined his father's business as a salesman, traveling in Pennsylvania. In 1870 he married and moved to Marcellus, Michigan, where, in August 1872, his second son, James Ashbury Allison, was born. In 1874 the family returned to Indiana, moving to South Bend, and then in 1880, to Indianapolis. Noah Allison had been a traveling agent for the National Surgical Institute and in 1882 he joined with Benjamin Nixon to form a knitting and hosiery manufacturing company, Allison & Nixon. In 1883 he and his brothers formed the Allison Knitting Company.

Noah Allison's Coupons

In 1885 Noah Allison launched a new phase of his career, one displaying some of the innovation and uncommon determination that would later serve his son so well. As America's consumer economy grew increasingly complex, retail business was often done on credit. Many debtors could not, or would not, pay their debts. So Noah Allison and George W. Abell organized the American Creditors Association.

Two years later Allison was president of the business, and apparently ready for new challenges. In 1888 Indianapolis was a thriving center of regional business and trade. Didn't the city need a trade publication? Certainly. So Noah Allison, experienced and observant businessman and articulate writer, saw another opportunity for his talents—in the world of publishing. He moved his collections company to more spacious quarters and simultaneously began to edit and publish the *Indiana Trade Review*. Like most newspaper operations of the era, the *Review's* equipment lent itself to job printing and bookbinding. But Noah was not like most other editor-publishers. He found another angle.

Noah Allison had helped merchants collect their receivables. Now he conceived a profitable way to help the debtors. Since his wholesale grocery days when he worked with his father, Noah was keenly aware of how poorly many men handled their money, drinking and gambling it away on payday.

Noah initiated a system among local merchants so that many necessary commodities could be paid for with scrip instead of cash. On payday a man would buy booklets with coupons good only for, say, groceries at a certain store, and valid only when detached by the grocery store clerk.

Buying a coupon book at a small discount, a man could get more groceries than if he used cash. The grocers did cash business and got their money in advance. All over the country retailers, mine and mill operators, and company stores clamored for coupon books. The ink and paper suppliers barely kept up with the demand at Allison Coupon. Noah brought his three oldest sons into the business and moved to bigger quarters in 1890.

But Noah Allison was not to enjoy the fruits of his prospering business. With his untimely death that very year, his wife, Myra, became proprietor of Allison Coupon and the three oldest sons—Wallace, James, and Dillmore—became directors. Placed under the management of prominent Indianapolis attorney John Berryhill, the company prospered and grew, moving to larger quarters five times in ten years, finally locating in 1904 on East Market, with Berryhill as president, James A. Allison, vice president, Wallace S. Allison, secretary, and Dillmore C. Allison, superintendent.

Workmen building the Panama Canal between 1904 and 1914 were paid in part with Allison coupon books. In Army posts nationwide the familiar perforations snapped steadily every payday. America's very first installment loans, in 1919, were repaid using Allison loan coupon books. And with appropriate coincidence, in 1922 General Motors Acceptance Corporation began using Allison payment books.

The children and grandchildren of Noah Allison operated the business until 1963 when it was sold to the Cummins-American Corporation.

Partners in Fortune

But, having married childhood sweetheart Sarah in 1907 (the marriage would end in divorce in June 1928), Jim Allison was destined for grander things than credit coupons. If destiny did smile on the young coupon company vice president in 1904, it can hardly have found a more apt bearer than Jim Allison's lifetime friend and soon-to-be partner, Carl Graham Fisher, the

Founded by Jim Allison's father Noah in 1885, the Allison Coupon Company of Indianapolis was operated by family members until its sale in 1963. This engraving of the home office was made in 1896.

"Fabulous Hoosier." Born in Greensburg, Indiana, Carl Fisher came to Indianapolis as a boy. He soon earned a name as a showman and promoter whose zany schemes were often shrewd and sensible. Like bicycles.

The penny-farthing high wheel bicycle, a common means of transport, was as mechanically fragile as it was awkward to mount. To Fisher that meant a bicycle repair shop. When the less colorful but far sturdier modern "Safety Bicycle" was invented, Fisher wasted no time arranging local sales franchises for several makes, and even one national franchise. With showy promotions and advertising, he built a mammoth bicycle business.

But Carl Fisher's interest in bicycles was soon overtaken by the motorcar. Launching into the auto sales business, Fisher used his sales savvy to profitable effect. By 1904 "Crazy Carl" was so busy with his prosperous automobile agency that he was difficult to catch up to. At least it seemed that way to Percy Avery who had called several times at the Fisher Automobile Co. trying to make an appointment. Finally, one day when Fisher was late for lunch, Avery managed to catch him and state his business.

Among other irksome and awkward equipment, early autos came equipped with kerosene lamps, only nominally superior to darkness. Newer models featured lights that burned acetylene from a generator

An imaginative and extraordinarily able entrepreneur whose career included major contributions in Indiana and South Florida, Carl Fisher was among Jim Allison's closest friends. The two collaborated in successful business ventures, including founding of the Speedway, from 1904 until Allison's untimely death in 1928.
Courtesy, Indy 500 Photos

that dripped water into a container of calcium carbide on the running board, creating illumination and annoyance in roughly equal measure. Percy Avery had an idea for compressing and storing a quantity of acetylene in a small steel cylinder. Even as Avery spoke, Fisher's canny mind was outlining a new venture. Hurrying Avery along to lunch, Fisher envisioned a business that would serve the whole automobile industry. All they needed was someone to put up the money.

And who was Carl meeting for lunch? None other than his good friend Jim Allison. Through the front window glass at Pop Haynes Restaurant, passersby might have witnessed some enthusiastically expansive gestures. Allison had to borrow part of the money, but in September 1904 Carl G. Fisher, James A. Allison, and Percy C. Avery formed the Concentrated Acetylene Co. with capital stock of $10,000. Offices were in Fisher's Automobile Agency on North Illinois.

By November they'd built a small plant at 28th and Pennsylvania and the business of concentrating acetylene got under way. Folks agreed it was Fisher's craziest venture yet. Everyone knew that compressed acetylene explodes with fearsome violence. They were right, of course, but Carl was unperturbed by the regular disasters at the Concentrated Acetylene Co. There was tremendous demand for compressed acetylene.

The Proof Is in the Racing

At the Indiana State Fair car races in Indianapolis in 1905, a festive Labor Day crowd cheered a victorious Barney Oldfield across the finish line in his Green Dragon. In the stands Carl Fisher and Jim Allison had been joined by some friends in the now-expanding Indianapolis automotive community: Frank Wheeler of Wheeler-Schebler Carburetor Company, Harry C. Stutz of Stutz Automobile fame, and Arthur Newby, principal owner of National Motor Car and Vehicle Corporation of Indianapolis.

Charles Merz drove one National racer, Jap Clemens the other, to smash world records held by the French Renaults. Supervising pit work for National was 26-year-old Norman H. Gilman, assistant to the superintendent of Newby's firm.

America's mounting fascination with the automobile may have been no keener anywhere than in this heartland of the nation. Allison's friends had each made strong commitments to the motor car that was fast becoming an immensely appealing consumer product. Together they were uniquely qualified to enhance the infant automobile industry's potential. Caught up in the zest of the competition, Allison and Fisher and their friends decided that day to arrange a 24-hour race to be held on the same track later in the year. Fisher naturally suggested that they light the track with acetylene lamps for night driving.

Jim Allison was chosen to manage the rousingly successful November affair. In a spirit of cooperation to advance American cars, automobile men from all around the nation came. New records were set, including raising the 24-hour distance mark from 789 to 1,094 miles.

The Indianapolis Motor Speedway

In the early hours of that November morning, someone, perhaps Fisher, said: "We ought to have a real paved and banked track with two-and-a-half mile laps. Then we'd hang up some real records." The friends not only agreed, but set in motion the historic wheels of the world's best-known and most enduring auto racing competition. In 1909 Allison, Fisher, Newby, and Wheeler founded the Motor Speedway after spending $72,000 for farmland. Jim Allison's real estate broker Lemuel (Lem) Trotter handled the deal. When the speedway was built, Allison was

secretary-treasurer of the firm and became president just after the 1923 race. He continued in that position until the project was taken over by Edward V. Rickenbacker and his associates in 1926.

The first race was held in 1909, and the first Indianapolis Speedway 500-Mile International Sweepstakes Race was run on May 30, 1911. From its beginnings, the race transcended mere sporting entertainment.

The gala event provided a common meeting ground for auto designers, engineers, manufacturers, and the world's premier racing drivers.

Ray Harroun, driving a Marmon, won the 1911 race; Joe Dawson won in 1912 with a National car, aided by his partner, Johnny Aitken. In the 1913 race as many foreign cars as American competed. But Arthur Newby's National was not entered, even though it had won 80 of 81 races that year. Newby, having gotten plenty of advertising, was tired of racing. Some thought the Peugeot's Indy victory due in part to help from 24-year-old Johnny Aitken who, with no National cars to race, had lent a hand to the French team.

Meanwhile, Back at the Gasworks

In March 1906 Fisher and Allison had moved their acetylene operations to a larger facility on South East Street. After Percy Avery left the organization, Fisher and Allison changed its name to Prest-O-Lite Company. Expansion prompted a series of moves to increasingly larger plants—East South Street, Oliver Avenue, and South Meridian. By 1911 the explosions abated and business continued to prosper.

Jim Allison felt sufficiently confident to begin construction of an elegant new residence that year, one of many projects that exemplified his determination to be associated with nothing but the highest quality. During the two years needed to build his Riverdale estate, Allison engaged renowned architects, builders, and artisans with instructions to create the finest structure possible. Complementing various exotic woods was white marble brought from Italy, and each major room was decorated in a different motif.

Coincidentally, in September 1912, at a cost just over a half million dollars, Prest-O-Lite completed a new plant of nearly 300,000 sq. ft. on land adjacent to the Speedway track.

A Track, a Race, a Team

John Aitken's friendship with Jim Allison offers a clue to origins of the Speedway and the Allison Company. Aitken approached Allison with the suggestion that Jim start a racing team. Allison was

Facing, top: Obviously pleased with themselves and their new racetrack on opening day in 1909, the four founders of the Indianapolis Motor Speedway posed with their distinguished guest from Detroit. Left to right, Henry Ford, Arthur Newby, Frank Wheeler, Carl Fisher, and Jim Allison.

Facing, bottom: Launching what would become one of the world's great sporting events, drivers cross the starting line of the first Indianapolis Speedway 500-Mile International Sweepstakes Race, May 30, 1911. The clouds of white smoke are caused by castor oil added to the fuel to improve cylinder-wall lubrication. Courtesy, Indy 500 Photos

Below, left: With the camera angle making his big Marmon appear to lean into the wind, Ray Harroun heads for victory in the first Indy 500. Harroun was widely regarded as an able engineer and car designer as well as a winning driver. Courtesy, Indy 500 Photos

Above: Begun in 1911 and requiring two years to complete, Jim Allison's spacious Riverdale home combined tasteful architecture, luxurious materials, and superb craftsmanship. The designer's generous use of glass fills the home with cascades of light and views of the rolling site.

Each of the principal rooms at Riverdale featured a distinctive decorating motif. The Sun Room, filled with tropical plants and furnished with rattan and bamboo furniture whose cushions were covered with bright floral print, evoked the Far East.

intrigued. He apparently had little trouble enlisting enthusiastic agreement from his friends Fisher, Wheeler, and Newby. Accustomed to personal success and borne forward by rising national and regional optimism, Jim Allison and his comrades eagerly took up the new challenge implicit in Aitken's urgent wish to race again. They quickly assembled three racing teams, starting with the Indianapolis Speedway Team Company. The founding date of this company that would one day emerge as the Allison divisions of General Motors is September 14, 1915.

Below: Luxuriant in cool marble and elegant palms, Riverdale's Aviary glowed with sunshine and the opulence of a Moroccan palace. Persian rugs graced the marble floor around the crystal-fountained pool.

At a cost of more than a half-million dollars, in September 1912 Prest-O-Lite completed a plant of nearly 300,000 sq. ft. on Main Street near the Speedway track. The company had already made Jim Allison and Carl Fisher millionaires.

Below: John Aitken, shown here before the 1911 Indy, in 1915 urged Jim Allison to form a racing team. In part at Aitken's suggestion, Allison and his partners formed the Indianapolis Speedway Team Company. Aitken was named manager, chief engineer, and ranking driver. Courtesy, Indy 500 Photos

Not unexpectedly, its manager, chief engineer, and ranking driver was irrepressible Johnny Aitken.

Indy Successes and a Man Named Eddie

Successful driver Ray Harroun was also a talented engineer who designed his own racer and persuaded the Maxwell Motor Car Company to build it. Allison and Fisher sponsored the necessary team, calling it the Prest-O-Lite team. And, making his first appearance in the Allison story, "colorful Eddie Rickenbacker, 'heavy-footed go-like-hell-till-bust,' who never won a race because he burned up his cars before finishing," was hired to manage the team and be its lead driver. In years to come, the aggressive young Rickenbacker would more than once play a fateful role in the Allison corporate drama.

The First Shops

Under the banner of their Indianapolis Speedway Team Company, Allison and Fisher put up a shop in a rented building on Georgia Street in downtown Indianapolis. Here they redesigned and rebuilt domestic and foreign cars for the races, including a fleet of Peugeot racers bought by Allison. For two years they were unsuccessful. Late in 1916 a somewhat discouraged Allison said, "Let's quit fooling around. This thing of running the cars out on the track for testing and then running them back to the shop three miles away is a nuisance and inefficient. Let me take over the company and I'll build a real shop out near the Speedway where it will be convenient." All agreed, and Allison became sole owner of the Indianapolis Speedway Team Company, while Fisher retained the Prest-O-Lite team. The little shop near the track was built, staffed with the finest craftsmen, and equipped with the best tools obtainable.

Norman Gilman Joins Allison

In December 1916 Allison and Aitken talked about finding a replacement for their shop superintendent who had quit. Coincidentally, John Aitken's friend Norman Gilman had just submitted his resignation as assistant superintendent at National Motors. One evening before Christmas, Gilman met with Jim Allison at Riverdale. The meeting would ultimately meld one man's passion for quality with another's practical vision.

On January 1, 1917, Norman H. Gilman became chief engineer and superintendent of the Allison Speedway Team Company. Aitken moved up to vice president and general manager. Allison remained president of the 20-man operation.

In that same year, 34 Prest-O-Lite branch plants were in operation. Fisher and Allison were already millionaires. They sold the 30,000-share

Surrounded by the paraphernalia of Allison's busy shop in Plant 1 on Main Street, shop superintendent C.L. Trosky, far left, confers with a colleague in April 1920.

Howdy Wilcox drove his Allison-commissioned and meticulously re-worked Peugeot to victory in the 1919 Indy, the last race in which Jim Allison's team would participate. Allison sold his cars and began his Florida development work while the engineering company sharpened its focus on aviation engine technology.

controlling interest in Prest-O-Lite for $9,000,000, but Allison retained large blocks of Prest-O-Lite and Union Carbide & Carbon stock.

A Nucleus Evolves

With Indianapolis a beacon for racing car drivers from everywhere, the shop of the Allison Speedway Team Company soon became a recognized center not only for pre-race honing of thoroughbred race cars, but also for the day-to-day business of refining the modern automobile. Here top mechanics explored pioneering designs and precision manufacturing problems for the following year's entrants.

But pervading the shop's operation on the corner of the Prest-O-Lite lot was James Allison the perfectionist, constantly demanding something new, something challenging, never satisfied with things as they were. No project or policy remained uninfluenced by his wide-ranging intelligence, judgment, careful preparation, dignity, and quiet manner. One observer overheard Jim tell a workman, "I want you to remember that this is not just another machine shop. Whatever leaves this shop over my name must be the finest work possible." That statement was his creed.

The First World War Comes to Speedway

With their best-available tools and equipment, the shop staff worked on new race car designs and models under the direction of Aitken and shop superintendent C.L. Trosky, while secretary and treasurer Luther Langston tended to financial and administrative matters. But on April 17, 1917, the morning after America declared war against Germany, Allison gathered his crew and said, "Quit work on the cars, but keep our men and continue to pay them."

Unable to reach Fisher or Newby, Allison phoned the newspapers to tell them there would be no more races until the war was over. Then he turned to Gilman and said, "Go find out how we can get war orders rolling. Take any jobs you like, especially the ones other fellows can't do, anything that will help us get started. Don't figure costs or wait to quote prices. We'll take care of that later." Indeed they would, and with Norman Gilman's leadership and a new name—Allison Experimental Company—Jim Allison's fledgling firm would soon begin making its way in the world.

Jim Allison and Florida

Having given his team its charter and the resources for its accomplishment, Jim Allison would wield his influence from a distance.

After the war ended, Allison commissioned a winning car for the 1919 Indy, then abandoned racing and sold all his cars to aviatrix Ruth Law, who used them in barnstorming and exhibition work.

Jim Allison, in association with Carl Fisher, then began a second phase of extraordinary achievement, in Florida real estate industries. He built an aquarium in Miami whose collection of marine fishes earned worldwide distinction. He also built a hospital in North Miami Beach. Active in the city's civic and business life, genial Jim Allison soon became one of the most widely known winter residents of Miami Beach. His large and handsome home on Biscayne Bay's Star Island became a meeting place for sportsmen, captains of industry, and celebrities. A director of the First National Bank of Miami Beach and principal owner of the Miami Ocean View Company, Allison worked closely with his friend Carl Fisher to spearhead the development of South Florida.

A Life of Its Own

Certainly the company's roots lay in the advent of the motor car. But almost from inception, the process of exploring new avenues that led to dependability, speed, efficiency, and utility steered the Allison group toward imaginative technical solutions and bold approaches to fundamental use of power—its generation, its control, its full range of possibility. Just as it would forever alter the nation's perspective of the world, the first World War brought the first glimmer of potential greatness to Jim Allison's tiny enterprise next door to the Speedway. That potential was unprepossessing enough, contained as it was in a set of drawings hastily executed over five feverish days in a Washington, D.C., hotel room.

The 1919 Indy field prepares for the start of the first race following the 500's wartime suspension. Courtesy, Indy 500 Photos

OFFICIAL SPEEDWAY PHOTO No. 10833

CHAPTER 2
Emerging

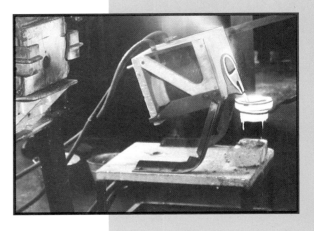

*Allison Experimental Company,
its people, its character, its place in
Indianapolis. The military
establishment, World War I;
the Liberty engine. Gears, bearings,
diversification; Rolls, Wright, and other
customers.
Allison Engineering; Norman Gilman
and the search for a core product.
Death of Jim Allison.*

Allison's historical links to American aeronautical and vehicular development assured the company its early place at the forefront of two industries to which it continues to make touchstone contributions.

In the four years preceding World War I, Jim Allison's wealth permitted him to pursue his interests in the vanguard of automotive development. He assembled a cadre of imaginative engineers and mechanics and provided them with quality tools, equipment, and facilities. American industrial development was changed forever when Europe was plunged into World War I. Overnight the carefree cheering for swift new race cars in Speedway faded. From London and Paris came a clamor for swift new warplanes for the recently-developing art of aerial warfare. The outbreak of the Great War meant aero engines, lots of aero engines.

Anxious men in cities not so distant from Indianapolis were soon developing a powerplant that would profoundly influence American aviation and give Allison's little company its steppingstone to international distinction.

The Curious Origins of a Hasty Hybrid

Even as Prest-O-Lite had been rising from the noise of its first years in Speedway to light the auto driver's way and generate the capital that funded the Allison Speedway Team Company, in Ohio the motorcar was being further sophisticated. In Dayton, home of the Wright brothers and the powerful National Cash Register Company, NCR vice president and chief engineer Edward Deeds hired a young fellow named Charles Kettering from Ohio State University to electrify the cash register.

Kettering had observed that a small electric motor could carry a huge load for short periods—nifty for adding machines and coincidentally providing a welcome relief for weary motorists who had to "get out and crank" to get their auto engines turning when Deeds applied Kettering's idea to auto starters. In 1908 he and Kettering formed Dayton Engineering Laboratories Company (Delco) to build electric starters, introduced on 1912 Cadillacs. Deeds next designed the first eight-cylinder car, the 1914 Cadillac. From this modest beginning Kettering launched an unparalleled career with GM that would repeatedly touch Allison fortunes.

Edward Deeds remained interested in cars and motors and, when World War I erupted, he joined Kettering and dam designer Harold Talbott to organize the Dayton-Wright Company, with Orville Wright as vice president and consultant. When the U.S. declared war, Deeds went to Washington as a member of the Aircraft Production board, of which Hudson Motor Car Company's Howard Coffin was chairman.

With a $640 million appropriation, the board drew up a plan to deliver 50,000 airplanes to France in one year's time. Put in charge of aircraft procurement, Deeds decided that aircraft development efforts should focus

on a single engine.   Legend has it that he locked two auto engineers in a Washington hotel room and in five days they produced a design that would become the historic Liberty engine.

"The engine," writes aviation historian Carl Solberg, "had automobile stamped all over it—eight cylinders, water-cooled, a Delco battery instead of magnetos." Redesigned with 12 cylinders like Britain's Rolls-Royce and reworked yet again, it passed into high volume production as America's principal aero contribution to the Allied war effort.

Doing the Necessary

Jim Allison's prompt commitment of his shop resources to war production quickly launched a flow of challenging design and manufacturing jobs, including high speed crawler-type tractors for hauling artillery and battlefield equipment, Whippet tanks, tank tracks, and production superchargers. The staff grew to 50, then 100, plus a temporary complement of 150 draftsmen to create and coordinate the reams of drawings needed to insure that parts built from them would work together. Production workers routinely logged 60- and 100-hour weeks.

But of all the projects, the most significant came from the Nordyke & Marmon Motor Company, who had government contracts to build both Hall-Scott engines and Liberties. Interchangeable manufacture in those days

Someone once asserted that aircraft engines are made up of equal parts of metal, sweat, and paper. From drafting rooms similar to this one in Speedway c. 1922, flowed the acres of drawings needed to accomplish engine design and rework during WWI.

Among the diverse war machines built under contract by Allison between 1915 and 1918 was a Caterpillar-type half-track field support vehicle.

required a complete, meticulously precise master model that became the standard against which factory-made parts were measured. Allison constructed two master model Liberties from Production Board drawings, together with a full set of tools, jigs, dies, fixtures, and gauges. By war's end Allison had also built several hundred Liberty engines in-house. Ultimately, 20,478 were produced by a wide range of U.S. engine makers. Perhaps 10,000 reached Europe. On Armistice Day 1918 the remainder lay in shipping crates at Wright Field.

Probably not featured on recruiting posters was this WWI tracked, gun-carrying vehicle, typical of the military contract work undertaken in the Allison shops in Speedway during the First World War.

Among licensed manufacturers of Liberty motors was Nordyke & Marmon. This device, engraved in four colors, emblazoned certificates presented to employees in December 1918 when the company was honored by the Bureau of Aircraft Production. In October the plant had turned out 308 engines, 246 percent over their quota of 125.

NORDYKE & MARMON COMPANY
ESTABLISHED 1851
INDIANAPOLIS, IND., U.S.A.

The Allison Twelve

Wartime work, particularly with the Liberty engine, had challenged the Allison people. They were eager for fresh opportunities. Throughout the 1920s Gilman and his staff steadily shaped the company's mastery of high performance engine technology and the parallel challenge of transmitting power into propulsion. Projects ranged from indulgent and futuristic to daring and standard-setting, but each deepened the Allison pool of knowledge and skills.

Among the special pleasures of Jim Allison and his affluent friends were big boats and yachts. Carl Fisher, for example, used his 80-foot *Sea Horse* to commute from his Long Island estate to his Manhattan offices and for seasonal voyages between New York and Miami.

When Allison acquired his 72-foot *Altonia II* soon after the war, he found no satisfactory marine engine of the needed size on the market. He asked Gilman to set about building an engine worthy of the Allison name. Reviewing final specifications with his employer, Gilman objected that they could not make a profit on such engines. Replied Allison, "Norman, we're not running a job shop for profit. Your job is to build the best engine possible." And so they did, announcing in 1920 the Allison Twelve marine engine. Derived from the Liberty, but much refined and more robust, it was intentionally heavy, with cast-iron cylinders instead of welded steel and a massive manganese- bronze crankcase-bedplate. Finished with the precision of an aircraft engine, it was completely waterproof, unprecedentedly smooth and quiet, generated 425 hp at 1,500 rpm, and was priced at $25,000. Offered as an accessory for the large engine was the Allison Lite, a four-kilowatt power set with a GE generator driven by an unusually compact and quiet 500-lb. Allison four-cylinder L-head gasoline engine.

In gray enamel, gleaming bronze, and sparkling nickel plate, the 4,400-pound masterpieces were given almost reverent treatment on their trip to the fitting-out basin. A dozen were produced: four for Allison, two for Arthur Newby, two for Carl Fisher, and four to sell. Fitted with her twin Twelves, *Sea Horse* could achieve 26 knots, *Altonia II,* 30. In their years of service on the Atlantic, the engines performed faultlessly, becoming a legend among East Coast yachtsmen.

The Gilman Bearing

The surplus Liberties stored in Dayton warehouses, however, were not so reliable. While they boasted modern engineering, with crankshaft and connecting rods of heat-treated alloy steel, and tungsten-steel exhaust valves, they also shared with most of that era's aero engines a grave shortcoming: crankshaft and connecting rod bearings that routinely failed after only

Carl Fisher's 80-ft. Sea Horse, fitted with a pair of Allison Twelve marine engines in 1920, sizzled along at a flank speed of 26 knots. Fisher used the yacht to commute from his Long Island mansion to downtown Manhattan and in Miami.

Arrayed c. 1920 are five machines that helped to establish Allison's reputation for quality. On the floor are a precision reduction-gear assembly for the Liberty and a V-drive marine gear that allowed a level-mounted engine to drive an angled propshaft in a compact hull installation. On stands are the four-cylinder Allison Lite generator set, a Liberty, and the Allison Twelve marine engine.

Something of an indulgence, only a dozen Allison Twelve marine engines were built, for the yachts of Allison and his friends. Adapted from the Liberty design and priced at $25,000, the 425-hp engines became famous for their reliability and durability.

The Allison hallmark stamped on a part or cast into the coverplate on an engine became synonymous with excellence.

An inventive engineer and manager, Norman Gilman not only handled the day-to-day operations of the company during its early phases as general manager and chief engineer, but assured its future success by developing the steel-backed bearing and tirelessly pursuing conception and development of the V-1710 engine from 1927 until his retirement in 1936.

about 50 hours. Whether in service or during upgrading tests at Allison, this flaw continued to nag. One engine, for example, was rebuilt and fueled with 20% benzol to increase horsepower from 450 to 500 only to thrash its bearings to junk in 31 hours, a noisy disappointment repeated with engine after engine. Not inappropriately, it was Norman Gilman's analysis and insight that led to a fix for the Liberty and a new product line for Allison.

In the Liberty's connecting rod design, the bearing rigidly clamped into a forked rod worked laterally on the outside of a bronze shell that distorted out-of-round under heavy engine loads. With dimensional stability lost and stresses no longer distributed uniformly, the bearing simply disintegrated, usually sooner rather than later. Gilman calculated that a steel shell, with twice the strength and three times the stiffness of bronze, would adequately resist distortion. To make the shell itself was straightforward, but to obtain the needed soft metal bearing surface on its outside proved more complex. Extensive experiments led to heating the steel form to a bright red and casting molten lead-bronze around it, then machining the cooled bearing surface to fit. The process was a complete success and extended the Liberty's service life from tens to hundreds of hours.

One result was a series of Army contracts to retrofit new bearings to surplus Liberties, usually in lots of 1,000. One 1928 Liberty contract totalled $1 million. More important, the superior bearing technology provided spectacular performance improvement in newer powerplant designs, and soon Allison was supplying bearings to engine makers worldwide. For the Wright Aeronautical Company's Whirlwind engine, they made bearings with the bronze on the inside instead of the outside. The most celebrated Whirlwind was the one that so faithfully powered Charles Lindbergh's *Spirit of St. Louis* through the long Atlantic night of May 19, 1927. Pratt & Whitney ordered the bearings for their new air-cooled radial Wasp that was introduced in 1925. Even the English came calling.

John Goldthwaite (who would become Allison's assistant chief engineer, and to whom the authors are indebted for his 1979 reflections on the company prepared for Indiana University's oral history program) recounted one of the earliest in the rewarding transactions with Britain's Rolls-Royce of Derby—a relationship that endures today.

"They came and asked us to license them to make the bearings. They had copied ours, tried to replicate them. And they made bearings that were better looking than ours, better in every way, except they didn't work. And what it came down to was the microstructure of the bronze. The real secret of the thing was the way they were cooled. After our bearing had the metal poured into it, it was immediately quenched in water. And that caused the metal to freeze very quickly and gave us a microstructure that happened to be favorable. Rolls-Royce played square with us. We shared the process and they paid us a license fee."

From 1927 the bearings became a major portion of the firm's business, helping to sustain Allison well into the 1930s. The process was kept secret from everyone because patents were not granted until years after it went into use. The delay was caused because patent officials maintained there was nothing new in the process. They finally yielded, and proper legal protection was granted to the Gilman bearing.

The First Reduction Gears

The wartime jobs also gave Allison engineers their first opportunity to explore high speed gearing,

One key component of Gilman's steel-backed bearing was precise casting and quenching of the copper-lead (bronze) surface. Workmen pour an early pot cast during the bearing's development phase at Plant 1.

In a display prepared for the 1933 Chicago World's Fair is a pair of connecting rods with the Gilman bearing in place on the shaft end. Arrayed around the rods are other steel-backed bearings of various sizes.

A typical V-12 crankshaft, with six of its twelve connecting rods installed (because the rods are paired, only four are visible), shows the design of the forked blade at the shaft end and the quality of the overall finish. The right-hand end is fitted with roller bearings.

SMOKING

a field in which Allison has remained preeminent for six decades. Their first application addressed an elementary fact of propeller-driven flight: aero engines generally produce power more efficiently at much higher rotational velocities than those at which propellers efficiently produce thrust. The goal was (and remains) an engine of low weight running at high speed to develop ample power linked to a propeller to run at lower speeds to deliver maximum thrust. That translated into gear reduction.

There were no such mechanisms in this country yet and many engineers believed it impossible to make gears light and strong enough to withstand airplane engine speeds. That sort of practical challenge was already a shop specialty to be met with one characteristic Allison approach: implement a sound design with unprecedented precision. Explains John Goldthwaite: "We had to run gears half again as fast as the handbooks would permit. But the limit existed because gearing was never accurate enough. When even minute irregularities in the gears came around too rapidly, they pounded each other and broke. We felt that if the gears were

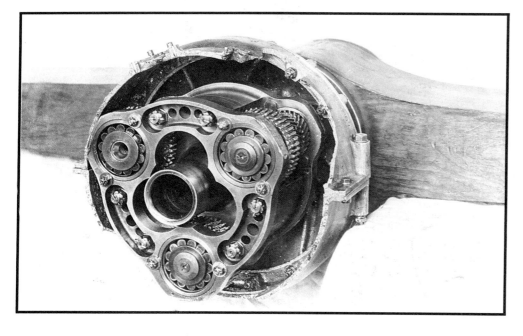

While the history of this reduction-gear assembly is lost, the splintered prop, fractured case, and abraded bearing frame indicate severe impact during rotation. Even with the gears themselves damaged, however, the main assembly and bearings remained intact.

made with sufficient accuracy, those irregularities would be reduced to harmlessness. And that was true. So our gearing was based on very high precision, using the right alloy steels and giving the right heat treatment. Proud of their work, the men on the line gave us that precision."

Of several firms invited to compete under a Navy contract, Allison succeeded in adapting a British reduction gear design. Refinements included a two-speed Liberty engine with gearing and clutches, followed by several Liberties converted to single reduction. For much of the 1920s, Allison was the only company actively pursuing aircraft reduction gears and supplied them to Wright Aeronautical and to Curtiss as well as for military developmental projects.

And the Odd Job

Supplementing bearing and gear work was the manufacture of a high-speed, Roots-type blower for airplane engine manifold boost in the middle 1920s, prior to the advent of modern centrifugal turbosuperchargers. Allison's early models were used in government laboratories for high altitude research in South America, Italy, France, Germany, and Great Britain. The world altitude record was held for several years by Pratt & Whitney engines equipped with Allison Roots-type superchargers.

The firm's reputation attracted more than one inventor looking for developmental and even financial support. Among these inventors was a fellow named Lasley who provided Allison with what was probably the company's first hands-on exposure to gas turbines. In 1928 Lasley brought rough designs for an aircraft gas turbine that would drive a propeller through gearing. He handled combustion using a gas turbine adaptation then coming into use in airplane engines linked with a supercharger blower developed by General Electric. But he needed reduction gears because the turbine ran around 30,000 rpm, the propeller at 2,000.

Manufactured by Allison around a National Aeronautics Advisory Committee design, this early Roots-type supercharger was a prestigious addition to the company's product line. In more refined editions, Roots blowers are still produced by Allison Transmission for Electro-Motive and the Detroit Diesel Corporation.

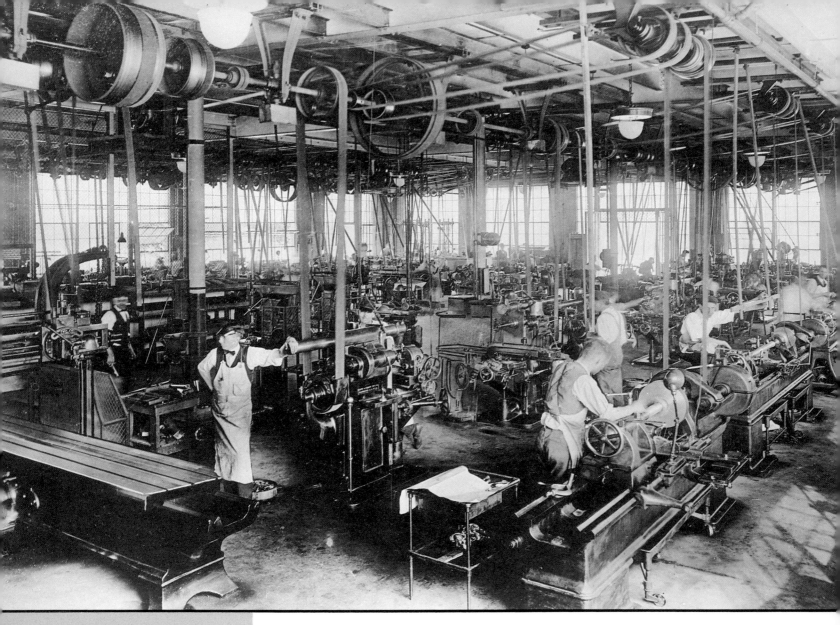

Gone is the illusion of the specialty shop in Plant 1 by the mid-1920s as the Liberty uprating and other work grew, replaced by this forest of overhead-belt-driven lathes, drills, grinders, and presses.

From Lasley's designs the Speedway crew completed the propshaft, centrifugal compressor, thrust bearings and gears, and machined the turbine and blower as a job shop, not as a financial partner. (When the turbine genie arrived again in 1944 with an unrefusable offer, the Allison welcome would be rather more receptive.) But in 1928 the Allison men knew next to nothing about gas turbines. Nor could they find anybody who knew more: others had attempted them, none had succeeded. "They were beautiful little 100-200 hp things," mused Goldthwaite about the Lasley machines forty years later, "and we made lovely gearing for him. But his combustion end never did work."

The Staff

Norman Gilman, who had run the company as vice president and chief engineer since Aitken's death in 1918, was a competent engineer who had taken an engineering course with a correspondence school, a not uncommon practice at the time and generally respected in the engineering fraternity. He had a vision for mechanical proportions and a natural aptitude for figuring things out—yet he greatly admired anyone who had mastered college mathematics.

After 1927 the staff always included at least one graduate engineer, and for some time that role fell to John Goldthwaite, whose Purdue degree in chemical engineering had covered a fair amount of metallurgy. All the engineering staff had competence in mechanical design and knew something of stress analysis. Lou Langston was corporate secretary-treasurer and also private financial secretary to Jim Allison, while office manager M. Wilson handled day-to-day business details and correspondence.

One Man's Ideal

Finances varied from year to year because the shop was occupied with so many diverse things. One project would make a small profit, another might lose a bit. Jim Allison's only charge was, "I want the Allison name something to be proud of." And if the shop occasionally attempted the impossible, Allison would be pleased that they were doing things that nobody else had the nerve or the vision to tackle. Indeed, Allison's unique engineering company reflected his personal ideals more than it did his ability to generate and manage wealth.

Despite his prosperity, Allison was conservative—and aware of his investment. During one of his yearly visits to the plant to see how things were running, he reminded Gilman and Goldthwaite, "Even a millionaire doesn't like to lose too much money." Recalled Goldthwaite, "If we lost some, that was all right, but the idea was we'd break even."

During the 1920s, Jim Allison's energies shifted from his Indiana engineering and manufacturing roots to the tides of real estate development sweeping across South Florida. His working hours were spent planning and building in real estate-frenzied Miami, his leisure hours on luxurious fishing yachts in the Gulf Stream. Allison's zest for the Indiana Speedway shop was steadily fading. Perhaps the single remaining emotion was pride. One contemporary recalled hearing Allison speak of turning the company over to his employees.

Another Man's Vision

This almost imperceptible change affecting Allison Engineering was apparent to Norman Gilman, who occasionally voiced his concern to colleagues. Gilman believed the company should have a solid product line to ensure continuity and security for the staff to whom he felt a keen

Looking southwest, across Main to 13th Street, c. 1923, both buildings of Plant 1 in Speedway are visible. Jim Allison's office occupied the southeast second floor corner of the south building.

Right and facing: These elevations of the first building of Plant 1 were prepared by the H.L. Bass Company in 1917 when the 81-foot chimney was added and modifications to the rear of the structure were made.

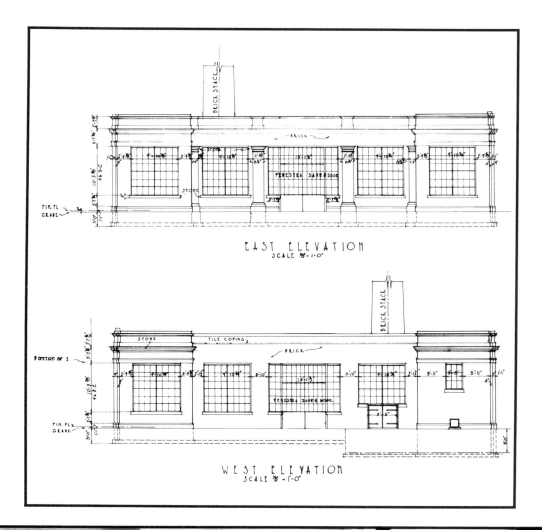

EAST ELEVATION
SCALE ⅛=1-0"

WEST ELEVATION
SCALE ⅛=1-0"

Individually-powered machines replaced the overhead belts to provide lower sound levels, better light, and greater productivity throughout Plant 1, c. 1920s.

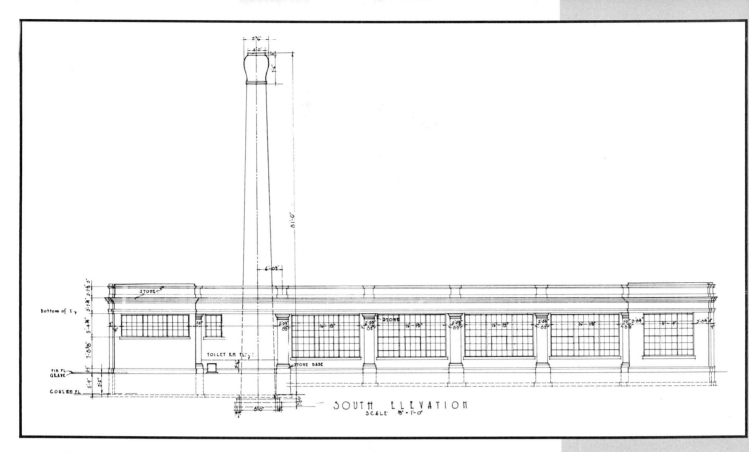

SOUTH ELEVATION

duty. The gears and bearings were a promising start, but something else was needed. As the decade waned, Gilman began to consider an idea that might just solve a whole array of problems. Airplanes were getting bigger and bigger, operational requirements ever more demanding for both civil and military aircraft. It probably wouldn't be long before designers would be looking for much more powerful engines, perhaps even as powerful as 1,000 horsepower.

The Founding Era Ends

Norman Gilman may have been pondering the challenge of product continuity in late July 1928 as he readied the Allison plant for an anticipated visit of the founder and owner. But the visit was not to be.

Beneath a banner headline, the *Indianapolis News* front page of Saturday, August 4, 1928, recited the facts:

"After an illness of only a few days, James A. Allison, widely-known Indianapolis capitalist and one of the founders of the Indianapolis motor speedway, died Friday evening at his Indianapolis estate, Riverdale, on West Riverside Drive, of bronchial pneumonia. Mr. Allison Sunday afternoon was married to his secretary, Miss Lucille Musset of Miami, at the home of Carl G. Fisher, Montauk Point, Long Island. The day following he contracted a heavy cold and on Tuesday started on a business trip to Indianapolis. He became seriously ill while on the train and on arriving here Thursday morning was taken to his home where his condition steadily grew worse. Mrs. Allison was at the bedside when the end came. Allison, fifty-five, was widely-known in the American automotive world, and through his extensive business and real estate holdings in Indianapolis and in Florida. Burial will be in Crown Hill cemetery."

As always with the death of one so vital, accomplished, and involved, personal sadness and tributes flowed to the family and the company he created. In the sorrow of the moment, tomorrow was of little interest to the public.

But for the lively enterprise Jim Allison had begun and nourished in Speedway, tomorrow could not wait. Even as probate lawyers reviewed the Allison estate, executives in Detroit were preparing to launch the Allison Engineering Company on the next leg of its journey to the future.

CHAPTER 3
Establishing

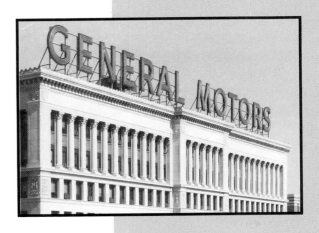

180905

Allison on the block, bidders, buyers, and plans; the Fisher brothers of Detroit. General Motors and fledgling aviation, industry contexts; GM acquires Allison. The aero engine in 1929, air- vs. liquid-cooling; Prestone. Gilman, the 1,000 hp engine; beginnings of the V1710. Army Air Corps and Navy engine ideas; airships, fighters, carriers, and politics.

*Previous pages, left: Its
developing reputation in
gears and shafts led Allison
to a series of contracts with
the Goodyear Company and
the U.S. Navy for work on
the Navy's rigid airships.
This c. 1932 view of the
Akron shows the general
layout of her eight angled
propeller drives.
Right: From the outside, the
airship propeller installation
was a great deal tidier, as
this view of the modified
Akron suggests.*

Whatever the Allison Engineering Company may have been when its engineers and craftsmen headed home for supper and the weekend on Friday afternoon, August 4, 1928, Jim Allison's company was something else when they came back to work Monday morning.

For Norman Gilman and the staff, the next few months were certainly marked by anxious moments. But the work of the company continued uninterrupted while Allison executors and attorneys sorted out the estate. Because all his life Jim Allison had shared his interests, desires, and pleasures enthusiastically with close friends and colleagues, his executors knew how he felt about the company he had founded and its place in Indianapolis. That may be one reason why Allison Engineering was put up for sale with the stipulation that offers would only be considered from buyers intending to maintain its assets and operations in Indianapolis for a period of 10 years.

In any case it made good business sense that the company's worth as a going concern was greater than its value as lifeless property and equipment. Given Allison's complex and specialized operation, however, it was evident that viable interest would probably have to come from outside the Indianapolis business community.

Changing the Guard

Several prospective buyers were approached, but none were willing to accept the stipulations. Two offers came from the East—one from Wright Aeronautical, the other from Consolidated Aircraft. Wright proposed to truck away the machinery they could use and offer jobs to interested staff at their Paterson, New Jersey, base. Neither company wanted to run a plant in Indianapolis.

A third offer late in the year from a Michigan group was far more attractive. Not only were the buyers prepared to accept the estate's near-half-million dollar valuation of Allison Engineering assets, but they readily affirmed their intention to leave the firm intact and operational. Details of the sale were confirmed, and on January 1, 1929, nominal control of Allison Engineering passed to Fisher & Company of Detroit. Eddie Rickenbacker was named president.

Fisher & Company?

Neither public nor company records of those first months of 1929 reflect concern about one element of the purchase that to some must have caused alarm. There was speculation that perhaps brothers Lawrence P. and E.J. Fisher had more in mind than operating a small, specialized engineering company in Indiana. The brothers were not just owners of Fisher & Company, but also members of the executive committee of General Motors Corporation, then actively exploring opportunities for GM in the emerging aviation field. Some observers believe that in the purchase of Allison Engineering the Fishers were acting on behalf of General Motors, which would buy Allison in its own right just 90 days later.

Other facts support the Fishers' stewardship role, and an early clue may have been a visit to Gilman's office one afternoon early in March 1929. A well-dressed fellow walked in and asked to look around the shop. He introduced himself this way: "I'm Charles Wilson, vice president of General Motors, and we're thinking of buying this place."

This is the stuff of legend. The documentary evidence is less colorful. First, the eventual sale to GM was disclosed through the Marion County Probate Court, which was also assured by GM of the corporation's intention to maintain Indianapolis operations. Second, GM's March 26,

1929, appropriation request covering the Allison purchase authorizes purchase payment to Fisher & Company "at the price paid by them plus 6% interest during the time they have held *the investment* (emphasis added)." Actual authorization records show the effective purchase date as April 1, 1929. Interestingly, GM president Alfred P. Sloan, Jr., did not announce the transaction publicly until May 24. The May 25 edition of the *Indianapolis Star* reported the purchase price as $525,000, and added, "Included are the two Speedway buildings and 14 adjacent acres. Eleven additional adjoining acres were purchased on March 24." The March GM documents show some $800,000 committed to the project—$600,000 for the initial purchase plus an additional $200,000 for improvements. Allison records show earnings of some $240,000 for 1929.

General Motors and Aviation

GM's purchase of Allison was only a small element in a much larger scheme. During the 1920s the aeroplane was moving from romantic fantasy into practical utility. Not unrelated to the glamour associated with aviation as a result of the first World War and its aftermath, the 1920s generated hundreds of aviation-oriented enterprises: visionary designers, daring pilots, aerial circuses, route mappers, airport- and airplane-owning movie moguls, aeroplane and engine makers who soared one day but crash-landed the next. Hundreds of pioneering companies were formed, bought, sold, merged, reformed, and dissolved. Some thrived.

After April 1, 1929, Allison references to "the corporation" and "Detroit" would evoke the image of the 15-story building at 3044 West Grand Boulevard in downtown Detroit—the 20-million-cubic-foot General Motors Corporation headquarters building completed in November 1920.

Astute corporate observers were not long in recognizing the enormous commercial potential of aviation. Charles Lindbergh's transatlantic flight in May 1927 was high drama and made an authentic hero of "The Lone Eagle." Historians now recognize the event as a milestone that effectively legitimized aviation to the general public.

Public acceptance meant that aviation was entering the economic mainstream. For companies properly prepared, aviation's commercial promise could be fulfilled. A number of the most influential managers at General Motors, including Charles Kettering, Charles Wilson, and president Alfred Sloan, Jr., intended to see that the corporation was indeed prepared.

The Allison acquisition was only one, and the smallest at that, of General Motors' commercial aviation-related acquisitions in 1929. The larger investments exceeded $23 million and included a 24 percent interest in Bendix Aviation Corporation and 40 percent in Fokker Aircraft Corporation of America. The long-range GM view was summarized in the 1929 annual report: "GM, in forming this association with the aviation industry felt that, in view of the more or less close relationship in an engineering way between the airplane and the motor car, its operating organization, technical and otherwise, should come into contact with specific problems of transportation by air. Through this association GM will be able to evaluate the development of the industry and determine its future policies with a more definite knowledge of the facts."

Indeed, GM was to "evaluate the development of the industry" by investing at one time or another in every major aspect of aviation, including airplane and engine manufacture as well as airlines. Among the companies which GM owned outright or had a major interest in were Fokker, General Aviation, North American Aviation, Eastern Air Transport (later Eastern Airlines), Transcontinental Air Transport, and Western Air Express. Writing years later, Alfred Sloan said of the Allison purchase: "By our standards, it was a small operation: the company had fewer than 200 employees in 1929, and manufacturing facilities occupied only about 50,000 square feet of floor space. We considered it to be only of minor importance in our plans to enter the aviation industry. Yet as events turned out, we were to make Allison our principal link to the industry."

Allison's size was not imposing by GM standards, but the particulars of its work in progress were both technologically interesting and filled with commercial and military possibilities.

By the mid-1930s, the two buildings of Plant 1 had been connected and handsome raised-metal signage added.

ALLISON X-4520 ENGINE
AIR COOLED X TYPE

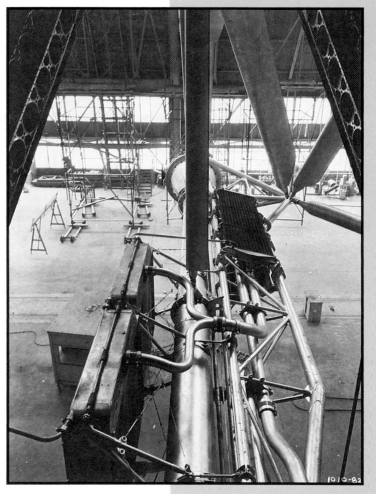

Strength in Diversity

The company was a major player in the era's brief excursion into rigid airships, the zeppelins. For the Navy's *Shenandoah* in 1923 the shop designed and built reduction and reverse gearing, extension shafts, and vibration dampers. Next came an invitation from Goodyear to bid on construction of a prototype extension shaft gear drive. Said John Goldthwaite, "We agreed on condition that if it tested satisfactorily on the flexible test stand at Akron, we would build all eight devices for the ship, and spares—an attractive bit of business. They gave us a set of tentative drawings and agreed to let us build the drive system as we saw fit. It involved a very long shafting which had not been used in aircraft before. It was entirely successful at about 50 or 75 hours testing. They were very much pleased with it."

For the first engine of its own design for the military, Allison in 1924 built a 4,520-cubic-inch experimental X-type, 24-cylinder air-cooled engine that generated more than 1,200 hp. Although the Army Air Corps abandoned interest in huge single-engine airplanes before the Allison could be used, the monster motor was considered significant enough for display at Chicago's Century of Progress Exposition ten years later.

Airships and Diesels

The airship shafting job led to Allison's earliest work with diesel engines four years before GM itself began development of the type. The first Zeppelin-type airships were gasoline powered, but both the U.S. Navy and commercial operators were attracted by the long-range capabilities of the diesel engine. At the Navy's request in 1927, work was begun in Speedway on a six-cylinder, in-line engine with intake ports on the bottom, four exhaust valves, and a Roots-type blower, with

Top, left: The first engine whose basic design originated with Allison was the X4520, a 24-cylinder, air-cooled engine built in 1924 for the Army Air Corps.

Above: Viewed from inside the airship envelope, the layout of mounts, radiators, and plumbing for the German Maybach 600-hp engines and their Allison gears and shafting can be seen.

Apparent in this disassembled airship angle drive is the unit's substantial structure and precision finish, essential for smooth and reliable operation.

43

Allison's development of diesel engines started four years before GM itself began research on the type. For the Navy in 1927, work was launched on a six-cylinder, 900-hp unit that weighed less than 3,000 lbs. By the time the engine was developed, the Navy had abandoned lighter-than-air operations.

During their brief but dramatic moment in aeronautical history, the great rigid airships offered visions of practical and economical civil transport as well as military utility. The Akron, pictured here, crashed in a storm of New Jersey in April 1933, killing 73.

projected horsepower of about 900 and a weight of less than 3,000 lbs. By the time the engine was actually developed, the Navy's interest in lighter-than-air operations had ceased as a result of a series of fatal airship crashes.

Before their demise airships contributed another element of innovation at Speedway. The Navy's zeppelins—*Los Angeles, Akron,* and *Macon*—were powered with German Maybach engines that produced under 600 hp and weighed 2,500 lbs. Anxious to re-engine the ships with more powerful, American, engines, the Navy contracted with Allison in 1931 for a fully-reversible engine in the 650-hp class that would run at about 2,400 rpm. After several years the engine passed preliminary type qualification, and two were built for flight test installation on the *Macon.* Workers were literally bolting the shipping boxes together to ship them to Sunnyvale, California, when the *Macon* broke up in the Pacific on February 12, 1935.

Shaping a Plan

For Allison the airship episodes were a useful exercise in design innovation. But with the GM acquisition, Norman Gilman's postponed search for a product to sustain Allison began to move toward serious implementation.

At its May 14, 1929, meeting, the General Motors Operations Committee appointed a special project committee for newly-acquired Allison. Its members were Charles Wilson, Ormand Hunt, Charles F. Kettering, and Norman Gilman. Its charge: "To consider the airplane engine program and formulate a plan for the Allison Engineering Company to decide what types of engines for aviation we should build."

Well before that meeting Gilman had a detailed vision of what they ought to build: a replacement for the obsolete Liberty, a wholly modern engine that should be powerful beyond anything yet attempted.

How Much Power?

As the air transport business was beginning to grow up and the Army was beginning to re-equip after World War I, Gilman had watched the increasing speeds of airplanes and the growing need for power. Said Goldthwaite, "Each year the Army would introduce a new plane with a little more power and a little more speed, you know; they'd have a competition. Gilman plotted a curve of the annual power increases. 'Look, Johnny,' he said, "1925 is this, 1927 is this, 1930 is this, and so

The Macon, *shown emerging from her hangar at Moffett Field in California, was scheduled to be fitted with specially-designed 650-hp Allison engines when she was lost at sea off Point Sur in February 1935.*

forth, and it's going up. Somebody had better start an engine aimed at 1,000 horsepower."

From the Liberty, the Allison design team had unsurpassed knowledge of water-cooled engines. Having spent years refining that one design, they knew what to avoid, particularly the difficulties of cooling and differential metal expansion. They were determined to design for high temperatures from the beginning and minimize the distortions common when aluminum and steel are present in the same structure. Next they agreed to plan for a 1,000-hp unit that would begin at a relatively conservative 750 hp, a power level they thought could be "sold" to the military.

Breaking the Water Barrier

Part of the Liberty's success lay in its cooling system. Water-cooling offered high mechanical reliability through inherently rugged construction where heat dissipation can be precisely controlled. But, reliable and powerful as it had become with Allison modernization, the water-cooled Liberty was critically design-limited. Its front-mounted radiator's huge surface area presented enormous wind resistance at higher speeds. But about 1927, someone conceived the idea of changing the coolant from water, which boils at 212° Farenheit, to Prestone (ethylene glycol) which boils at 357° Farenheit, permitting operation at proportionally higher temperatures. The higher the temperature, the smaller the radiator needs to be because high temperature is easily radiated. That allowed radiators small enough to streamline engines until their air resistance was negligible.

In an early experiment with Prestone, the Curtiss Airplane and Engine Company modified their water-cooled V-12 Conquerer. Problems with the penetrating and solvent characteristics of the coolant resulted in hot spots in the cylinders even though engineers went to 300° and a much smaller radiator.

In June 1929 Gilman hired Harold Cominez, an experienced aircraft engine designer. Early the following year he assigned Cominez as project engineer to devote full time to design of an engine to be called, from its basic configuration and the displacement capacity of its 12 cylinders in cubic inches, the V1710.

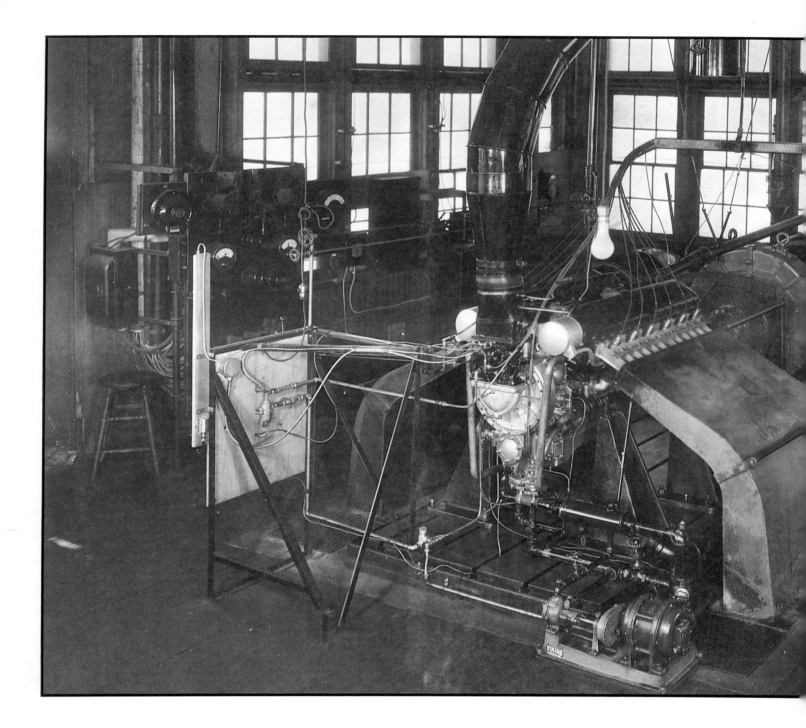

CHAPTER 4

Anticipating

Selling the V1710 to the military.
Hazen, Detroit, and making the V1710
work. It flies. The altitude question,
supercharging and turbosupercharging;
Congress and defensive weaponry;
the P-40. The first large orders;
manufacturing on the threshold of war;
tooling up, the best of Allison meets the
best of GM. Extraordinary tasks and
men; labor, plant, process.

On May 7, 1929, Norman Gilman and his team began to sketch the V1710 engine design, not unsurprisingly with some of the Liberty's best elements and some from the Rolls-Royce V1650. The premise was an engine of 750 hp at the outset with plenty of room for growth to 1,000 hp. But neither the Army Air Corps nor the Bureau of Aeronautics at the Navy were sufficiently convinced by Gilman's enthusiastic advocacy to commit development money. Even in Detroit the power seemed excessive. If that much power should ever be needed, they said, multiple engines would be best, not single engines. From on high came the message: aim at 800 hp.

By 1939 Gilman's power projections would be vindicated by events. But technical innovation is often impeded by short-term thinkers. Conservative military men were not persuaded by oral argument, however eloquent. They could be convinced by accumulated operational evidence, but that took time. Slowly the inevitable need for greater speed and load-carrying capacity gained momentum. Airframe makers and armed services planners began to appreciate the potential virtues of the more powerful, streamlined liquid-cooled engine concept.

The First Order

Gilman's first sale was modest. On June 26, 1930, the Navy Department's Bureau of Aeronautics contracted for design and development of the GV1710A engine rated at 750 bhp at 2,400 rpm. The prototype was delivered March 12, 1932. After three failed attempts, the engine passed its 50-hour acceptance test in September. But by then, Navy brass had committed the branch to air-cooled engines because they were shorter—then just one ring of cylinders—and easy to store on aircraft carriers. And, in a controversy made meaningless 20 years later, its detractors viewed the liquid-cooled engine as fragile prey to the first stray bullet to puncture the plumbing. So the Navy's Allison prototype and in-service Packards were shoved over the side in favor of Pratt & Whitney and Wright radial air-cooled Wasps and Cyclones.

Early Optimism

The V1710's next seven years had a touch of period Hollywood about them. In hushed drafting rooms, industrious model shops, roaring test cells, austere military offices, and even airplanes in flight, plucky engineers, devoted craftsmen, hard-headed colonels, and a corporate vice president assembled to create a plot that was accelerated by the looming specter of a world war.

Meanwhile, back at McCook Field (later Wright Field, then Wright-Patterson Air Force Base), the Army Air Corps engine people expressed cautious interest in the engine design Gilman had shown them three years earlier. They contracted for a modified model, the XV1710-1. It was acceptance tested in June 1933 at 750 bhp at 2,400 rpm. Caution turned to haste: with increased blower capacity, the engine was promptly uprated at 2,650 rpm and dynamometer tested at 1,000 bhp for 9 1/2 hours and at 90 percent power for 41 1/2 hours under favorable mounting conditions. Confidence reigned. The XV1710-3 was contracted for on March 29, 1934, and delivered to McCook for its 150-hour type test in June. On the 18th, an additional order for a similar engine, the YV1710-3, was placed, contingent on acceptance of the XV.

The 800-hp Threshold

The steep curve of optimism flattened abruptly. On the test stand, engines balked at power above about 800 hp, and runs were noisy, baffling, and short. Starting in June 1934, Gilman and the staff grappled with cracked crankcases, vibration-fatigued crankshafts, burned valves, fractured forgings, and sheared cotters. Months of seemingly endless test stand running and corrections forced Gilman to consider radical rework of the basic design. Finally, in March 1936, Gilman suspended the tests to reassess the situation. He arranged with GM engineering vice president Ormand Hunt for the support he needed from Detroit.

Ronald Hazen and Breakthrough

In the summer of 1933, a young engineer with impressive credentials had applied for a position at Allison. Gilman had hired him.

Wright Field, Ohio, would play a crucial role in Allison affairs from the day the company began business with the U.S. military. Headquarters for the Army Air Corps and later the United States Air Force equipment development, evaluation, and acquisition processes, today's Wright-Patterson Air Force Base remains one of the Gas Turbine Division's principal marketplaces and technical forums.

In 1917 the site, owned by Charles Kettering and Orville Wright, was leased by them to the U.S. Army Signal Corps, subsequently being sold to General Motors. The land was acquired by the government in 1927. Air Corps photo, October 1934.

Ronald M. Hazen had left the University of North Dakota at the outbreak of World War I, served as a master mechanic at the 7th Aviation Instruction Center in France, and was subsequently commissioned a lieutenant and pilot in the U.S. Army Air Service. In 1919 he resumed study at the University of Michigan and graduated in 1922 with a BS in mechanical engineering. After a stint at the GM Research Corporation at Dayton, Ohio, Hazen in 1923 completed his graduate work at the University of Minnesota. In 1927 he joined the Wright Aeronautical Company in New Jersey, and two years later was assistant chief engineer of Ranger Aircraft Engine, Inc., a division of Fairchild Engine and Airplane Corporation on Long Island, New York. Promoted to chief engineer, he supervised development of the Ranger 6- and 12-cylinder, air-cooled aircraft engines.

In the early 1930s General Motors Research Laboratories technicians in Detroit were working on a pair of two-cycle engines—a large flat opposed-cylinder unit for the Army, and a small radial for a $700 flivver airplane advocated by the Department of Commerce. Hazen had been invited from Allison to apply his Ranger experience to the projects, but ultimately the GM team concluded that two-cycle technology was not yet ready for either proposed application.

By 1936 the rise of fascism threatened a fragile European peace. Air power was being tested under murderous conditions in the Spanish Civil War. Even in the climate of isolationism in the United States, military preparedness was debated with increasing vigor.

At General Motors, where the Allison operation had been given division status in 1934, the engine project the corporation had been nourishing so steadily at Indianapolis moved higher on the corporate priority list. It became the subject of frequent meetings. So Gilman's inquiry to Hunt in Detroit was treated with the urgency it deserved. The necessary approvals were obtained, and soon Hazen was back in Indianapolis, this time as chief engineer, his first assignment to head up a revitalized V1710 team.

Gilman later said, "Since the very beginning of Allison Engineering I held the title of Chief Engineer, but when I decided to get Ron Hazen back to head up engineering at Allison, I felt that here was the man who should succeed me as chief engineer."

Focus on Fuel

Hazen quickly mobilized his lieutenants—John Goldthwaite, Carl Reynolds, Charlie MacDowall, Jud Buttner, Bob Heath—and set to work. He already knew precisely where they'd start. Part of the V1710 difficulty clearly lay in customer-required changes in engine configuration. From February 1935 Air Corps officials had insisted that all 10 contract engines be modified to fuel injection, necessitating complete redesign of accessory drives and housings, intake manifolding, and cylinder head ports, even though no supplier was yet building a satisfactory fuel injector. Thirty-five years later Goldthwaite reflected on those frustrating months: "It was too early to require fuel injection. Had they let us complete the engine with a carburetor, we'd have been years ahead. We should [have been] developing engines, we should have [had] engines in flight test, and we were working on this damn fuel injection, which took a lot of engineers' time, a lot of experimental time, to test in the engine."

Hazen's first big decision as chief engineer was to revert completely to conventional carburetion for the V1710. He wasted no time in lining up his allies in the anticipated battle with fuel injection partisans at Dayton. For his first meeting with the Air Corps engine people, he asked vice president Hunt to join him. There Hazen announced that, if allowed to proceed with his plans, Allison would have a qualified V1710 ready for production in a matter of months. The Air Corps people turned skeptically to Hunt: "Can we believe Mr. Hazen is speaking with any authority?" Hunt shot back, "Mr. Hazen is our chief engineer. What he says, General Motors will back up."

Hazen had thoroughly reviewed the cumulative V1710 data and confirmed his analysis with the staff: their two fundamental problems were fuel distribution and structural weakness. First, the fuel system put too much fuel in numbers one and six cylinders, and starved numbers three and five: one pair was overloaded, the corresponding pair underloaded. Overstressed during high power output, these cylinders simply failed. Second, complying with the Army's insistence on lightness, designers had left some components too light for the greater stresses imposed by higher power demand. Summarized Goldthwaite, "Light weight per unit of horsepower is essential, but you don't get it by cutting weight but by increasing power with what you have. So Hazen put extra metal where it was needed and eliminated other weak spots with improved castings."

The Type Test

Thirteen weeks later, on June 13, 1936, the first "new" YV1710-3 with redesigned intake manifolds and strengthened components was hoisted gingerly from the truck to begin its 150-hour type test. As the reassuringly steady roar in the cell passed the 140-hour mark, the Allison team in Dayton wired a cheery progress report to Gilman at Indianapolis.

But even as Gilman, who had been planning his retirement for months, asked his secretary to type a retirement letter for signing in the morning, a disqualifying crack developed on the engine's left cylinder head. A new head was installed and a penalty run begun; at 245 hours, the right head failed.

It Flies

Despite the failures, Hazen's group believed they were close to success. So did the military, who released the remaining eight contract engines for fabrication in September. Among the eight was YV1710-9, the ninth unit to be built, and the first to fly.

On a chill December afternoon, a small group of observers from Allison and the Army Air Corps watched a modified two-seat Consolidated A-11-A lift off the Wright Field runway. The flight's success had equal parts of Norman Gilman's dream, the skilled determination of Ron Hazen's able colleagues, and the character of the young company's late founder.

Said Gilman years later, "I cannot tell how we got any particular idea. You talk to one man and that starts you thinking, then someone else tells you something and that starts you off on another track. By and by your thoughts start crystallizing and finally you get a definite idea. But I do know that if it had not been for Jim Allison I would never have built that engine."

On April 23, 1937, the V1710 engine passed its 150-hour acceptance trials, America's first airplane engine to qualify at 1,000 hp. But plenty of work remained for the engine team, for airframe makers and installation engineers, and ultimately the division and the entire General Motors family.

Ironically, even though amassing 300 flight test hours on the V1710 over the Ohio and Indiana countryside, the A-11-A was essentially an antique aeroplane, ill-suited to flight test a 1,000-horsepower engine. The

Developed from a 1930 Lockheed design, 50 units of the Consolidated Aircraft P-30 were built in San Diego following the company's move there from Buffalo in 1935. Several of the ships were built as A-11s, a low-level attack fighter-bomber powered by a 675-hp Curtiss Conquerer water-cooled engine. This A-11-A served as the first testbed aircraft for the V1710.

The Curtiss XP-37, with YV1710-7 installed, was the second V1710 installation. The airframe, originally designed for a radial engine, is conspicuously hybrid, and was soon outclassed by the P-40. Capt. S.R. Harris of the Flight Test Section posed with the airplane in July 1937.

next two testbed airframes were some improvement—a Curtiss XP-37 adapted from its original air-cooled design in 1937, and Larry Bell's twin-engine XFM-1 Airacuda attack bomber of 1939. The Air Corps people were pleased enough to order 60 more V1710s; and Norman Gilman did, in fact, sign his delayed retirement letter, effective December 31, 1936.

A New Era for Allison

Anticipating the profound metamorphosis now underway for the Speedway operation, in mid-1936 Detroit had selected for Gilman's successor as general manager O.T. "Pop" Kreusser. He was a man respected for proven skills in large project management, particularly at the GM Proving Grounds and Chicago's Museum of Science and Industry. For about six months, Gilman and Kreusser worked together before Gilman retired.

At Speedway, Hazen's team suddenly faced a puzzlement carefully reported by John Goldthwaite: "You see, we built the engine to test on a mechanical and electrical dynamometer, to be bolted to the dynamometer stand, none of us dreaming that it had to be mounted later on in an airplane that didn't have a couple of horizontal steel stringers! They had to improvise ways to get that engine into a plane. Until we actually developed 1,000 horsepower with more than 100 hours testing, they never put an engine in an airplane. And when they did finally put an engine in an airplane, everybody was amazed at what it would do in the air—things nobody had ever dreamed of."

But the dreams were punctuated by plenty of tossing and turning as the new engine emerged from the relative security of the test cell to make its way in the world.

Out of the Lab and into the Sky

Early installations with Air Corps-stipulated turbosupercharging were disappointing. In March 1937 the first V1710-equipped Curtiss YP-37 performed below expectations, primarily because of high drag from the turbosupercharger and intercooler. On an early flight, the airplane was crash-landed after a supercharger fire and so was not available for the spring Air Corps Pursuit Competition. Installation of two D-type

The first multiple-engine V1710 installation came with the Bell XFM-1 Airacuda attack bomber of 1939. The pusher-type ship had expansive triple canopies, resembling the era's streamline concepts.

YP1710-9s in pusher layout for the Bell XFM-1, first flown in September 1937, encountered similar turbosupercharging drag problems.

Increasingly frustrated with problems which they were prevented by military stubbornness from eliminating, the Hazen team was eager to proceed with an altitude-rated engine with internal first stage supercharging. The Air Corps continued to resist.

Made for Each Other

Finally, in preparation for the November 1938 Pursuit Competition, Allison enlisted the support of Curtiss managers to persuade the Air Corps to fund one of the airframe builder's experimental XP-40 aircraft

*General manager "Pop"
Kreusser (left) and chief
engineer Ron Hazen visited a
test cell of an early V1710
around 1939. Under
Hazen's dynamic leadership
the engine matured through
early growing pains into a
reliable and production-
ready engine.*

*The Curtiss Pursuit of 1939
provided the V1710 its first
opportunity to prove the
merits of a 1,000-hp liquid-
cooled powerplant, in an
Army Air Corps competition.*

for mating with an
altitude-rated C-type
V1710 minus the
external
turbosupercharger.
The engine was
delivered in
September 1938,
but the competition
was postponed until
spring 1939.

For Allison,
Curtiss, and the Air
Corps, the results
were surely worth waiting for as the handsome and thoroughly modern-
looking XP-40 flashed through her trials at an astonishing 40 mph faster
than the previous winner. The revolutionary XP-40 left the remaining
competitors fairly lumbering around the course. Presumably, however,
Air Corps officers present were more judicious in their enthusiasm than
they had been in February with the Lockheed XP-38 prototype.

Lightning Strikes

In June 1937, responding to an Air Corps design competition for a high-altitude interceptor capable of speeds to 360 mph, Lockheed Aircraft Corporation designer Kelly Johnson and chief engineer Hall Hibbard had offered the winning Model 22. For the twin-engine, twin-boom contract prototype designated the XP-38, Lockheed chose counter-rotating C-type V1710s. The airplane made its maiden flight from March Field near Riverside, California, on January 27, 1939.

So dazzling was the silvery XP-38's initial performance that normally level-headed generals were persuaded to authorize dispatch of the lone prototype on a transcontinental speed record attempt after only five hours of flight testing.

On February 11 the XP-38 left March Field for Long Island's Mitchell Field. Pausing for fuel at Amarillo and Dayton, the Air Corps pilot sizzled along at speeds exceeding 400 mph. But, while letting down to Mitchell after an elapsed time of 7 3/4 hours, the pilot crash landed on a golf course. As a result, P-38 flight testing was delayed for many months.

The significance of the P-40 and P-38 successes was not lost on military planners in Britain and France, especially when viewed alongside parallel developments over Berlin. In April 1939 Fritz Wendel's Messerschmitt B-109 set a world's speed record of 469 mph: his engine was a liquid-cooled, in-line, 1,000-hp Daimler-Benz.

Great Britain had the excellent Rolls-Royce liquid-cooled Merlin, but its aircraft industry, unaccustomed to mass production, was hampered by lack of technicians, tools, and skilled labor. For much of the decade, the French had focused on domestic and overseas commercial air operations to the virtual exclusion of military aviation. Both realized the inadequacy of their defenses and moved to order the new U.S. airplanes and Allison engines. By May 1940 overseas orders were in hand for more than 4,000 V1710s.

Only General Motors

In Speedway and Detroit, even though management had been broadening Allison capabilities, the V1710 phenomenon was about to expand exponentially. The enormous depth and diversity of the far-flung General Motors Corporation would shortly transform its Allison Division from an engineering model shop into a production giant in a feat of unprecedented organizational ingenuity and energy.

Assistant Secretary of War Louis Johnson personally asked General Motors president William Knudsen that the corporation establish a plant for production of V1710 engines, even though the government could not then guarantee additional engine orders or fund the building.

In May 1939, a month before a contract for 969 engines was awarded by the Army Air Corps, ground was broken for the new 360,000-sq. ft. factory and office building that would be known as Plant 3. When production began there in February 1940, the Allison payroll had climbed from less than 600 the previous May to 1,702 employees. Schedules that had included perhaps 200 engines per year now projected thousands. And it was clear that experienced managers of every sort were the first priority.

Recruiting of men from the outside to fill these vital jobs was out of the question. Even had they been available, to shape an efficient team of men from different industries, accustomed to differing operations and procedures, would take far too long. But the immense worldwide GM organization with its firmly established corporate culture and diverse operations provided the answer.

While few GM people outside of Allison had ever seen an aircraft engine, they knew production. In coming to dominate the auto industry,

General Motors had refined methods and procedures which these men knew as intimately as they knew their faces in the shaving mirror. Soon highly experienced design and production engineers began arriving from all points of the compass to form the nucleus of key men around whom, with amazing speed and efficiency, an organization of more than 12,000 employees would be built by December 1941.

The "imported" executives in 1940 were as imposing as the tasks they undertook. In August, Frederick C. Kroeger, who as general manager of Delco-Remy Division was regarded as one of the best production men in General Motors, was named general manager of Allison. The new works manager was Bill Guthrie who, from his position as production head at General Motors' Opel works in Germany, caught virtually the last boat from a German port to the U.S. Under him were combined tooling, manufacturing, standards, inspection, and plant engineering. Bert Conway, general master mechanic from Pontiac, became general production superintendent; C.M. Jessup, production manager at Delco-Remy, became manager of material control; and R.C. Smith came from AC Spark Plug as chief inspector. Staff jobs in turn were filled with senior GM experts in the appropriate disciplines.

Among America's historic airplane makers, none has produced airplanes more consistently handsome or effective than Lockheed. Among the company's great successes was the 1937 Model 22/XP-38. As the P-38 Lightning, some 10,000 were built and powered with counter-rotating C- and F-type V1710s to become one of WWII's most successful warplanes.

The old timers were in their old jobs where their experience fit. And both above and below top management at Allison were more seasoned General Motors professionals: men like Robert K. "Bob" Evans, head of GM's engine group and a veteran of overseas production; Charles Kettering, the corporation's irrepressible research wizard; Ormand Hunt, the engineering vice president who had risen from the ranks through the Chevrolet mass production organization. All left their Detroit homes to take up virtual residence in Allison's Indianapolis offices where the lights seldom cooled.

Everything was orchestrated, and divisional location was no hindrance. The V1710 components were analyzed and matched against the particular strengths and resources of every GM manufacturing facility. Because of its fabled craftsmanship, for example, Cadillac took on the crankshaft, connecting rods, and reduction gears, while Delco-Remy specialized in aluminum and magnesium castings.

From Artisans to Neophytes

The immensity of the task in Speedway lay partly in the V1710 itself. It was a highly complex mechanism of some 8,000 parts that must transmit enormous stresses within precise tolerances under widely varying conditions, most of them severely punishing. A special responsibility accompanied every step in engine building: failure in service could kill a pilot.

Now, from the deft hands of the engineers and craftsmen who had created it, the V1710's destiny would pass largely into the care of earnest men and women with no previous related experience. The first machinists at Allison had come from automobile factories of Indianapolis, especially the National Motor Car Company. But now, there was no local pool of highly skilled labor.

As the agony of global warfare deepened, a transformed Allison Division was flexing its muscles in the unaccustomed role of manufacturing giant. General Motors the corporation and General Motors veterans had taken over and production began to grow. The 48 engines of 1939 became 1,153 in 1940 and 6,433 in 1941. Plenty of challenges remained, but the new team had made a gallant start. By December 7, 1941, some 6,000 V1710s were fighting in the skies over England, Africa, and China. The men and women who created those engines, however, had only begun to fulfill the limitless potential of the Allison organization.

CHAPTER 5

Triumphing

The V1710 and Allison at War.
Engine development and engineering
philosophy; job shop and assembly line.
Relations with GM divisions.
Craftsmanship, testing, special problems.
Ed Newill; GM production experts and
management people; tooling, plant
expansion. Personnel recruiting, training,
labor unions. Morale, the "E" Awards.
Tigers, Warhawks, Lightnings, Airacobras,
and Mustangs.

Previous page: Workers assemble components to a V1710 block from which the cylinder head dowel bolts protrude and over which the cylinder heads will be carefully lowered later. On the left side can be seen connecting rods ready for attachment to their pistons. The middle front assembler supports two pistons while his colleague at left aligns a piston and its connecting rod.

Indisputably one of America's most imaginative and effective technologists and business leaders was electrical engineer, inventor, and long-time GM vice president Charles Franklin "Boss" Kettering (1876-1958). In his leadership role at GM, his judgment frequently affected Allison's destiny.

I n its early days Jim Allison's enterprise had enjoyed the freedoms and privileges of its founder's wealth. The people who worked in Speedway shops and offices concentrated their talent and energy on elegant solutions to technical problems, largely at a pace of their choosing, largely untroubled by marketplace realities.

Since 1929 Norman Gilman's group had fared better than many small companies, in part because of their integration into the General Motors organization. But they also generated current and potential products of genuine commercial viability. During the Depression years Allison had produced at a modest profit the bearings and reduction gears that became aviation industry standards. And in the V1710 they were creating a modern aircraft engine of unprecedented power and serviceability.

In 1939 this small Midwest engineering company was swept into preparation for war. Virtually overnight the comparative calm of design, fabrication, and testing of 14 engines in a decade and the measured production of bearings—the work of 500 engineers and craftsmen in two small buildings—erupted into a tumultuous frenzy of flat-out, maximum-volume production. Although the change must have been startling for Allison's Speedway staff, company decision-makers in Detroit and Indianapolis reacted swiftly with a characteristic midwestern practicality both balanced and resolute.

The GM Commitment

Having accepted the challenge of building as many V1710s as possible as quickly as possible, General Motors and Allison managers assessed their needs, established priorities, and began implementing a plan even as they marshaled their resources—people, raw materials, plant, and systems. Concurrent with William Knudsen's agreement to build the new plant in May 1939 came the crucial commitment of the General Motors organization itself. Its pool of management skill and experience was led by Alfred Sloan, Charles Wilson, Charles Kettering, and Ormand Hunt.

The Manufacturing Priority

In preparing to set up Plant 3, for example, GM experts studied V1710 drawings plate by plate, with Allison engineers at their side, to focus on design and construction for mass manufacture. Details were examined to devise the most efficient procedures for casting, grinding, drilling, heat treating, and assembly. Designers and process engineers negotiated possible modifications to ensure or improve speed, efficiency, quality. "Why is this part like this and not another way?" "Well, it must be like this because. . ." or "It could be changed like this." Having assessed the function and tooling requirements of every piece, they chose machines, tools, and fixtures to hold them, prepared needed drawings, and sent them to toolrooms in Detroit, Pittsburgh, Cleveland, and other machinery centers across the country, to be made.

They priced drills, milling machines, grinders, lathes—the whole array of conventional and special machines. They bought them, had them delivered on a specific date, and saw them oriented properly on the production line. From the time the tooling crew began their survey until the line was up and running, less than a year had passed.

There were a few glitches in the process when some key questions were not asked, or at least not in sufficient depth. Early Cadillac connecting rods, for example, were made precisely to Allison drawings. But, it developed, some drawings specified over-generous tolerances that led to inconsistent matching during assembly. Modified specifications swiftly solved the problem; and the quality of Cadillac's Allison work is legendary in Indianapolis.

Subcontracting within the corporation was a long-established part of GM's basic policy of "decentralized responsibility with coordinated control," in which "the primary responsibility for contracting, pricing, and production rested with each individual division of the corporation, subject, of course, to GM's over-all policies."

Among other divisions and subsidiaries providing parts for the V1710 were Chevrolet, New Departure, Hyatt Bearing, Delco Products, Packard Electric, AC Spark Plug, Antioch Foundry, Harrison, and Inland. From the beginning one distinction remained unblurred: the engine's manufacturing derived from the corporation, but its conception, design, and operational aspects were wholly the province of the Allison division.

Building Factories First

The quick efficiency with which Plant 3 construction progressed was partly due to Allison's staff architect J. Lloyd Allen. Allen had been hired by Gilman in the mid-1930s when prospects for the new engine suggested that perhaps 200 units per year might be built and the division was exploring an extension of Plant 2. Allen reviewed contemporary factory design standards and conferred with Allison engineers to master facility requirements for manufacturing and testing the V1710, from space and footing needs for each type of tool and machine, to work flow, ventilation, storage, and illumination.

Building the two-million-square-foot Plant 5 in Maywood in 1942 took barely four months. Construction time and scarce steel were saved with prefabricated components such as these pillars, called "thunderbirds."

Two electrical companies had displayed fluorescent lighting at the 1939 New York World's Fair, projecting commercial introduction in perhaps two years. Allison managers persuaded the companies to advance their production, and 20,000 five-foot-long tubes were delivered in 1940, the first large installation of the cool and efficient lighting type.

The Plant 3 exercise was only the first of several that would accommodate 1943's peak employment of 23,019 people and production of more than 3,000 engines per month. Building expansion continued practically without interruption.

In 1942 ground was broken for the two-million-square-foot production facility, Plant 5 in Maywood. Because of the critical steel shortage, ingenious devices such as gigantic wooden pillars called "thunderbirds" were used. From the laying of the foundation to occupancy took only three months and 27 days. In that time a factory was built that covered an area equal to 20 city blocks. The plant was visible evidence of an Allison legend that a new factory was in use before the architect's drawings were completed.

Building a New Team

Pop Kreusser had ably supervised Allison's initial expansion of manufacturing capability, drawing upon his leadership and organizational experience. However, as the enormity of Allison's 1940 production buildup was evidenced, he was among the first to recognize Allison's acute need for an expert in high volume production, and with zest he took on a new assignment as director of training and service.

When 50-year-old Frederick Kroeger arrived from Delco-Remy in August 1940, the wisdom of choosing a general manager with the strongest possible background in high volume work was proven. A 1911 electrical engineering graduate of Purdue, Kroeger had begun his career at General Electric, then moved to Remy Electric Company at Anderson, Indiana, before serving in World War I as head of electrical equipment design for the Army Motor Transport Corps. After his Army tour, Kroeger rejoined Remy, which became part of General Motors in 1918. He was made chief engineer in 1921. Elected to a GM vice presidency in December 1940, Kroeger masterfully directed the teeming complexities of Allison's mushrooming war-driven buildup.

Recruiting and Qualifying

Perhaps the greatest initial challenge facing the new Allison was to recruit, qualify, select, and train thousands of new workers. They would be called upon to perform the demanding tasks of manufacturing elaborate, precision aircraft engines in previously unimagined quantities. To meet Plant 3's initial employee complement of 3,500 and an ultimate work force of more than 20,000, the personnel department (headed from 1939 through 1944 in sequence by R. Kremer, J. Brophy, K.H. Hoffman) was soon hiring 100 people each day from all walks of life—interviewing, checking backgrounds, arranging health examinations, setting up personnel records.

Matching Men and Machines

More than half of the new employees, whose average age was 22, came from nearby Indiana communities, and from Ohio and Illinois. Because the area had no particular tradition of mechanical technology, there were precious few skilled machinists in the labor pool. The solution had two parts: first, intelligent and responsible candidates willing to learn; and second, manufacturing processes that could be accomplished satisfactorily after a relatively short training period. An overwhelming

majority of the men and women who flowed into the Speedway and
Maywood employment offices proved themselves more than worthy of the
Allison challenge.

The machine toolmakers were up to their challenge as well. By 1940 it
had become possible to perform many precision manufacturing
operations with machines that were run not by machinists but by
operators: the essential skill and precision could be built into the
machine and its fixtures, a method already partly developed in the
automobile industry.

The thread grinder and the contour projector illustrate the process
that made possible not only the manufacture of 21,381 V1710s in a single
year, but indeed the entire nation's stunning industrial outpouring of
World War II. Precision
threading was essential
to the V1710. Formerly
it took a master
machinist several days
to set up and produce a
precision ground
thread on a bolt. Now
the Excello Company in
Detroit had designed a
machine to do it
automatically.

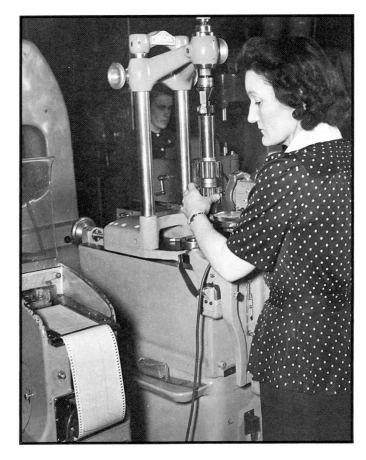

"We thought when
we bought the first one
that we'd need to have
the most skilled grinder
in the shop to run it
because it was a delicate
operation," said
Goldthwaite. "But
Excello said we didn't
need an experienced
grinder. So we got a
boy whose total shop

*After initial assembly, each
V1710 was run in on the test
stand and its performance
measured against standard
before being torn down,
cleaned, and inspected prior
to final assembly and
shipment. In the foreground
a single engine's sub-
components, including the
block and protruding
headbolts, are laid out for
assembly. To the left are
banks of pistons (two banks
required for each engine).*

*During the wartime
emergency, America's
factories needed many more
workers than the traditional
male labor pool could supply.
Thousands of women
nationwide answered the call
for help and proved
immensely able in wide-
ranging assignments. Allison
plants employed large
numbers of women —31
percent of the work force in
1943, most of them new to
the workplace. Here an
inspector verifies dimensions
on a gear-checking machine,
c. 1943.*

experience was in the barn doing minor repairs on his father's tractor, and we put him on that thread grinder. The manufacturer's representative instructed him, and within a couple of days he was doing more accurate work in making screw threads than any of our skilled machinists had ever imagined.

"The final measurement of the screw thread was made with a contour projector—like a slide projector but with a bolt in it instead of the slide—that projects a shadowgraph of the bolt with its screw threads magnified, say a hundred times, on the screen. There had been a few expensive contour projectors made before, but not for the kid on the thread grinder. Now there was a small projector with proper centers to mount a bolt on and a screen about six inches square."

Ultimately banks of thread grinders and counterpart machines for other processes were run by operators without previous skill but who were carefully selected and instructed. They were wide-awake young people eager to learn and to do good work. All they had to do was press buttons and work levers. Simple inspection devices were located beside each machine so that the operator could inspect the pieces as they were processed.

Training and Service

After Kroeger's arrival, Pop Kreusser assumed the enormous task of training Allison's burgeoning work force as well as the military and civilian personnel who would be maintaining engines in the field. Kreusser's front line "faculty" were 400 senior Allison craftsmen who introduced new employees to the world of precision machines, acquainting them with tools, processes, procedures—and the Allison universe.

A formal Training Department for V1710 service and maintenance was launched in July 1940, with two instructors and six students. By December 1943 the section had grown to 88 instructors and staff, with 11 zone offices worldwide. Facilities were leased from the Hercules Paper Box Company at Lafayette Boulevard and Holt Road from 1941 to 1945, and known as Plant 6. In addition to instruction, the unit included a

Building engines was only part of the job assumed in Indianapolis. The complex machines shipped from Allison's plants had to be properly operated and faultlessly maintained to perform satisfactorily. Training for pilots, engineers, maintenance staff, and other support people was a high-priority task from 1939 on. Service School manager Connie Martin reviews V1710 operating systems with a class of flying officers.

publications staff of 40 under Dick Tripplehorn, responsible for publishing operation and maintenance bulletins, parts catalogues, and manuals. Technical writers adapted material so it could be easily understood by both inexperienced draftees and longtime mechanics.

New Problems, New Solutions

Many of Allison's challenges arose at the frontiers of technology, in areas largely untrodden by any manufacturing organization. Early in the war Allison found existing sources inadequate to supply the intricate aluminum castings required to carry the V1710's high stresses.

At Antioch College near Dayton, Ohio, a professor and his wife had perfected the lost-wax method of casting art objects to exceedingly close dimensions in their small foundry. GM bought the foundry and hired the couple to work on applying their technique to high-strength aluminum parts. Their innovative work complemented two foundries set up at Anderson and Bedford under Delco-Remy to supply aluminum castings for Allison engines. These castings proved to be infinitely better than others available anywhere in the world—and at less than half the cost. At war's end Delco-Remy converted the Anderson foundry for its own needs and Allison purchased the Bedford Foundry. General Motors sold the Antioch shop back to the professor and his wife and paid them royalties on GM castings made with their process.

An instructor takes a new group of student mechanics through the intricacies of a V1710-E11's auxiliary stage supercharger assembly as a demonstration unit's impeller is fitted into its housing, c. 1943.

Shared Discoveries

Aviation has long been known for its sharing of technology, particularly in matters of safety. The common cause of patriotism further nourished the tradition among American aviation manufacturers. Membership in groups such as the Automotive Council for War Production, which met at plants around the country, allowed engineers to share ideas that could be carried back to their own plants.

At the Wright Aircraft Engine factory in Lockland, Ohio, near Cincinnati, for example, Allison engineers observed one of the industry's first automated systems for cylinder head manufacture. Wright had developed a continuous, fifty-foot-long automatic line to drill, bore, turn, tap, and thread the complex form of the air-cooled cylinder head. On a conveyor at one end of the line would start a casting or forging and at the first machine it would be clamped down in position for some operation. That machine would finish and the piece would be released to the next machine. After each process, a head with gauging equipment would

*Facing page: The major
models of Allison's WWII
engines in rear, side, and
front views. The top is the
2,000-hp V3420 of 1939: its
two Vs of 12 cylinders are
twinned V1710s matched to
a common block. Below the
V3420 are the 1941 V1710 F,
the lightest, shortest, and
most powerful V1710, used
in the prototype P-51 and
some P-40s, with left- and
right-hand rotation models
for P-38s; the C engine of
1940, the first production
engine for the P-40 and P-38;
the 1941 E for the P-39; and
the 1937 D (at lower left is a
D2 engine for the pusher-type
Bell XFM-1); at lower right
is the 1941 shaft and remote
reduction gear layout of the
E engine for the P-39.*

verify that the operation had been done correctly. The line required no operators, just a few men of inspector-level always watching to see that everything ran properly. Today, of course, most volume manufacturing is done that way.

Not by Machines Alone

Automated production by its nature tends to de-emphasize individuals' contributions to the finished product. Allison's necessary adoption of the process was no exception. Yet over time, memories of remarkable people endure among colleagues and in corporate records of every sort. One such engineer was Arthur W. Gaubatz, a University of Michigan-trained engineer who came to Allison in 1939 from Buick where he had been chief designer of their very successful straight-eight engine.

The V1710 at that stage was stubbornly defying efforts to correct fuel problems. Gaubatz devised a fuel control mechanism that solved the immediate difficulty and led to three separate patents. "On loan" from Buick, Gaubatz stayed with Allison until retirement in 1964, compiling 66 active, quality patents ranging from bearings to rocket motor controls.

Testing Keeps Pace

Among the most important aspects of aviation-related manufacture is comprehensive testing—because the consequences of in-service failure are unacceptable. As the V1710 was uprated in power output and adapted to various aircraft installations, new test procedures of every sort were devised. During a rash of connecting rod failures, engineer Goldthwaite devised a method of simulating engine loads on test rods at high speeds so the parts could be observed directly under load. Reported Goldthwaite: "So we built my little machine that pushed and pulled the rod with forces comparable to the engine's 20,000 lbs. Anybody would have thought that a connecting rod was just rigid, but you could actually see the thing shorten and stretch. When that's happening at speed, it just looks like rubber. And pretty soon it would break, always in the same place. Knowing the failure origin, we added about half an ounce of metal at the weak point and never lost another connecting rod to that cause."

Multiple V1710s

Responsible for coordinating the V1710's literally continuous model changes and modifications throughout its life was chief design engineer Charlie McDowall. The original C engine, the first big production model, had a fixed reduction gear ratio of two-to-one in a very long nose as originally requested by the Army for the P-40. New aircraft designs specifying different gear ratios and other changes required new V1710 models. Both the E model for the Bell P-39 and the F engine for the P-38 were designed and introduced without interrupting production, in itself a remarkable achievement. During one period, the average time between model changes on the line was just 40 days.

Simplification

Among other changes made to enhance manufacturing efficiency was the consolidation of sub-assemblies, a process which allowed the V1710's 7,000 individual parts to be reduced to 700 piece parts— separate production elements—compared to 2,300 piece parts for the Rolls-Royce Merlin. By way of illustration, parts in one sub-assembly were reduced from 38 to three by simply casting the part whole instead of building up bolted components. (Engine parts counts, it should be noted, vary by the counter and what's counted: with every nut, washer,

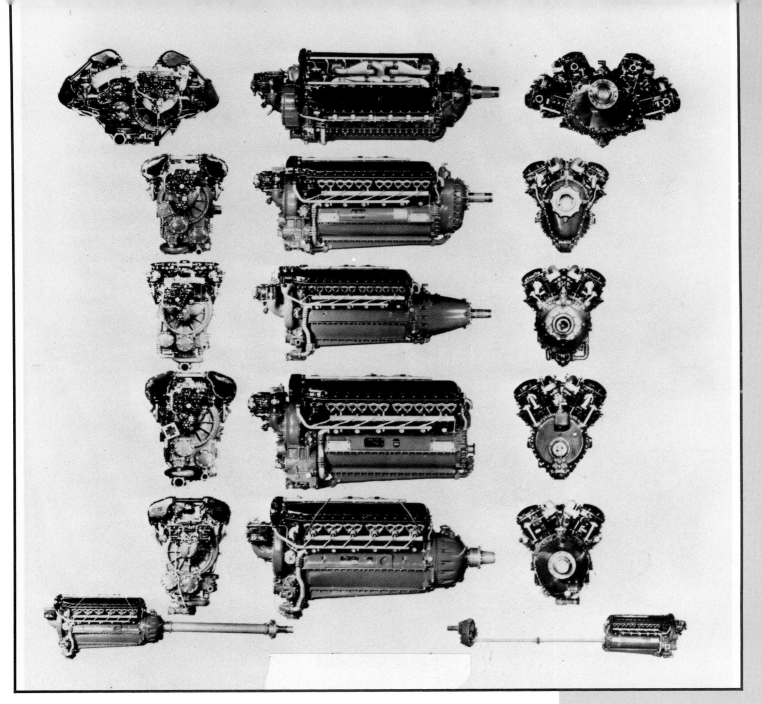

gasket, and cotter pin included, a random V1710 unit might run to more than 8,000 parts.)

The Life-Dependency Standard

Among the people who worked in the design rooms and on the production floor at Allison, noted one engineer, "there was a universal conviction that men were going to fly these engines, and if anything was wrong with them it would kill the pilot. We repeated that and believed it and acted on it. There were some scares where something did go wrong, where some defective part apparently passed. But when any suspicion arose that something might have been wrong, the first step was to shut down the shipping room until the problem was isolated and corrected."

Subsidiary Issues

Typical of the diverse problems that surfaced as production mounted was noise. Noise problems, both for the production and testing staff and for the community around the plants, had begun when rebuilt Liberties were tested on an outdoor stand with simple wooden walls and roof to keep the weather off the operator. Speedway City wasn't big then and complaints were often ignored. "You had to test the engines and they made noise and that was that." But testing at wartime production levels meant serious noise. The architecture and engineering books of the 1930s contained little noise data, most of it worse than useless. Pursuing their own original research and evaluation, Allison staffers pioneered noise reduction techniques, from environmental sound level assessment to anechoic baffling. Among Allison innovations were effective isolation of the test engine operator from the engine using compact electrical engine controls and sound-baffled chambers that drastically reduced noise output.

Noise in the Ear of the Beholder

In the course of their research, engineers supplemented technical discoveries with helpful people observations. Said John Goldthwaite: "Without going into the details of decibel meters, it turns out that noise is sound you don't like. If you do like it, it isn't noise; or if you are accustomed to it and choose to ignore it, it isn't noise."

In surveying the Speedway neighborhoods around Plant 3, Goldthwaite measured test engine sound levels at varying distances up to 10 miles away. "I stopped at a little grocery store to find out what people thought, and asked the woman behind the counter, 'What's that noise going on?' She said, 'What noise?' I said, 'That noise up there.' 'Oh,' she said, 'that's something about the engines up at Allison.' 'Well, doesn't it drive you crazy?' 'Oh, no,' she said, 'whenever I hear that noise I know the boys have jobs and my trade will be good.' Nearby, on the other hand, a woman was threatening to sue. Her glassware was falling off the table, and it was driving her nuts and she was going to sue us because of that noise. Two women living in houses practically side by side. One found the noise a good sign, the other headed for court."

A Matter of Costs

The price of the V1710 engine was at first "pretty much guessed." The 1932 prototype was almost arbitrarily priced at $75,000, and estimates of incurred development deficits from 1929 until the engine entered production range from $800,000 to more than $1 million. The contract unit price dropped to an historic low of $9,304 in 1945.

With no relevant experience at the outset of wartime production, cost estimates were crude. Managers executed military contracts on the understanding that when the company established cost records, the contract would be renegotiated and a new price set based on actual experience. Allison managers proudly noted that all the wartime renegotiations were initiated by the company. As performance

A V1710 is torn down for inspection after its initial run on the test stand, c. 1941. Visible on the left cylinder head are the rocker arms and valve springs for the valves which control the flow of fuel vapor and exhaust gases to and from the cylinders below.

improved, lowered costs were passed along in a lower price. The military initially opposed the renegotiations but soon recognized the consistent fairness of Allison pricing.

The V3420 Goes to Sea

While V1710s were destined to earn fame and glory in every theater of the war, an attempt to launch a naval career for its big twin brother, the V3420, resulted in less success—but plenty of entertainment. Responding to the threat posed in the Mediterranean by speedy Italian naval motor torpedo boats, the British designed a boat of their own—the Scott-Payne patrol torpedo (PT) boat. In 1939 the PT boat came to the attention of President Franklin Roosevelt, a notorious enthusiast of things naval. Soon several million dollars were allocated to develop a comparable vessel for the U.S. Navy. The Scott-Payne boat with its three Rolls-Royce Merlin engines was brought to New London, Connecticut, for demonstration.

With an eye on the 2,000-hp V3420 engine, the Navy invited Allison observers to see the British boat perform. Pop Kreusser and John Goldthwaite headed east. Well out to sea the British commander opened up the throttles and the PT boat roared and hissed along at an exhilarating 40-plus knots. The Electric Boat Company was contracted to build a U.S. prototype, the PT-8. Thinking that this might be a way to get its big engine into production, Allison agreed to participate, but with reservations. Goldthwaite was put in charge of Allison's part in the project.

The planned compromise was that Allison would supply two forward-only V3420s with connect-disconnect jaw clutches. The Navy would install a 600-hp marine engine for maneuvering and reversing because the big

Top: By contrast with 1943's comparatively comfortable engine test environment, this 1925 view of the Allison 24-cylinder, X-type 4520 engine shows the simplicity of an early test stand.

Among refinements developed during WWII were vastly improved powerplant engine test cells that included control and monitoring stations isolated from the running engine. An operator logs data from a V1710 in 1943.

engines were not designed to operate at slow speeds. Said Goldthwaite: "An airplane engine performs best in every way at high speed, and it doesn't idle very well. But you have to be able to back a boat up. And we refused to design a reverse gear for a single order, but agreed that for a production order we would design a proper marine modification that would do everything."

Unplanned compromises followed, reducing the aluminum-hulled PT-8 and her trials to a comedy of errors. The engines arrived at the Philadelphia Navy Yard and were installed. Next came the twin 30-foot prop shafts, specified by Allison as steel bored out with a quarter-inch wall, to weigh perhaps two hundred pounds. The Navy, to avoid the expense of the boring, installed solid shafts that weighed three tons.

"Then," said Goldthwaite, "they decided to send that thing from Philadelphia up to the Brooklyn Navy Yard in convoy with several wooden-hulled PT boats that were unable to withstand high speeds in rough open ocean. The PT-8, on the other hand, could go either very slow with her marine engine or very fast with her Allisons, and her metal hull was untroubled by the heavy seas. All the way to Brooklyn the wooden boats forged ahead as fast as they dared go without opening their planks until almost out of sight, then the PT-8 would open up and overtake them in a wild rush, to slow down again until the wooden boats caught up. That was the whole trip to Brooklyn, and that was the end of the PT-8."

A Change in Leadership

In April 1943 general manager Fred Kroeger began a leave of absence because of poor health that would culminate in his death 13 months later. From May through July, the general manager position was held by

The biggest of Allison's wartime engines was the mighty 2,000-hp V3420 that saw limited service in such test aircraft as the XB-19 and the XB-39, and a fighter that came too late for active service, the Fisher P-75.

Two V3420s found a brief, colorful career in this prototype patrol torpedo (PT) boat, the PT-8, built by Connecticut's Electric Boat Company in 1940. Production model PTs were engined with smaller, Packard-built Rolls-Royce Merlins. The whaleback hull design, intended to shed water quickly, originated in the Great Lakes ore boats of 1888.

Cy Osborn, who would later head GM's Electro-Motive Division in La Grange, Illinois.

Ed Newill Takes Charge

On August 2, 1943, Edward B. Newill was named general manager of the Allison Division (he would be elected a GM vice president in July 1948), beginning a 17-year Allison career during which he would lead the company through some of its most challenging and productive times.

Following graduation from the Georgia Institute of Technology in 1915 with degrees in electrical and mechanical engineering, Newill began work with Westinghouse Electric and Manufacturing Company in East Pittsburgh, Pennsylvania. In 1929 he joined GM to head the General Motors Radio Corporation. The following year he was named chief engineer and director of research for Frigidaire Division, becoming division assistant general manager in 1937. In 1941 Newill became assistant to the GM group executive in charge of the household appliance and aviation divisions. In 1942, with the formation of Eastern Aircraft Division, he was made assistant to the group executive in charge of Eastern Aircraft and GM divisions in Dayton.

Ed Newill had already earned a reputation within the corporation as a problem-solver, a leader who got things done. In approaching Allison's

During a summer 1945 visit to Maywood, P-38 pilot Richard I. Bong was "interviewed" by Allison general manager Ed Newill. Medal of Honor-winner Bong recorded 40 victories over Japanese aircraft in his Lockheed Lightning to become America's greatest air ace. Dick Bong was killed in a takeoff accident in a P-80 just weeks after this photo was taken.

The Air Corps' first technical representative assigned to Allison's flight test operations, Major Jimmy Doolittle was a favorite of company engineers and support staff. His "personal" P-40, in which he commuted to and from Allison on other assignments, was often used as a test plane. In 1943, the year after his famed Tokyo raid from the decks of the Hornet, Doolittle made a bond drive visit to Allison and was hosted by general manager Fred Kroeger, left.

subsequent corporate turning points, Newill would exhibit both imaginative flexibility and cautious conservatism. In 1943 he took charge of Allison's destiny with vigorous competence and a gracious charm recalled warmly by colleagues decades later.

Among corporate accomplishments Newill recalled with pride was the Frigidaire Division's production success in making the .50 calibre machine guns which Browning and Colt designers had loudly asserted could not be mass-produced. Not only were the weapons produced in huge volume and on schedule, but were much praised by battle-tested soldiers: "A GM gun always worked."

At Allison, Newill-led achievements included the inauguration of the massive manufacturing facility at Plant 5; the flight test facilities of Plant 10 at Weir Cook Airport; the research facilities of Plant 8; the transition from piston to jet engines following World War II; and the initial work with Allison turboprops that resulted in their preeminence in military aviation.

Edward and Zilpha Newill's three sons all went to work for the corporation—Edward J., with Delco-Remy; William J. with Delco Products, and Robert B. with Pontiac Motor Division. Grandson David B. continues the 60-year Newill tradition with the Allison Gas Turbine Division.

The UAW Comes to Indianapolis

Although the United Auto Workers (UAW) during the late 1930s had managed to organize practically all the General Motors divisions across the United States, Allison's first labor union agreement appears to be a September 17, 1940, pact not with the UAW, but with the United Aircraft Engine Workers, Inc., an independent union certified by the National Labor Relations Board (NLRB).

The earliest UAW Allison-related activity is a September 17, 1941, meeting called by UAW-CIO International representative John Bartee to obtain names of 20 members to go on a charter for Allison employees. On October 12, 1941, temporary officers were elected, among them president Merritt Allen. Early in 1943 the UAW made its first effort to organize Allison workers, obtaining enough signatures for an NLRB election in April. That organizing effort was unsuccessful.

In March 1944 election of the local's first permanent officers included president Paul Eberts and vice president Arthur Skibbe. That year an office was opened in the Knights of Pythias building on North Pennsylvania Street under field representative Anthony Probe. The Local began

publication of *The Rocket*, edited by F.J. Dalton of the International staff.

A second UAW representation drive resulted in an NLRB election on September 7, 1944. The UAW-CIO received sufficient votes to be declared the bargaining unit for the company. On November 22, 1944, the NLRB granted Local 933 full bargaining rights in Allison plants. Allison may have been the last of the General Motors' divisions to be organized by the United Auto workers, in part because the old-time machinists long resisted the idea that any organization outside the company itself might influence their professional affairs.

The Allison Spirit

Like much of the sentiment of America in WWII, from the perspective of half a century later a sense of the patriotism, community pride, and company loyalty that pervaded the Allison organization throughout the Second World War is not recaptured easily. Bond drives, plant visits by movie stars and military heroes, the winning of the Army-Navy "E" award, flyovers of fighters at employee picnics, and ceremonies to mark production milestones may seem quaint to a post-Vietnam generation. Nonetheless the cause was noble, its values enduring, and the accomplishment heroic.

More than nostalgia moves Allisonians to recall those homefront rituals. Dorothy Lamour, petite and glamorous with her entourage winding its way among the big machines on the shop floor and talking with workers. Bob Hope and Jerry Colonna ad-libbing to a delighted lunchtime audience. A sunny spring day rally in 1941 on Plant 3's spacious lawn, dignitaries speaking, a band playing. Then low thunder and a howling roar as a lone P-38 Lightning—flown by Allison test pilot Pinky Grimes—passes low,

In March 1944 Allison produced the 50,000th V1710. To mark the occasion, the milestone engine was "exchanged" for the first V1710 to have flown, "Old No. 9" of 1936. General manager Ed Newill joined with Maj. Gen. John Curry in an informal ceremony to mark the occasion.

Of America's movie stars during the Second World War, Dorothy Lamour was among the most generous in devoting her time to entertaining troops and headlining bond drive rallies.

The most visible symbol of the Army-Navy "E" award was the huge blue burgee to be flown from an honored company's flagpole. The 1944 banner is raised.

The company's wartime performance was, by every standard, phenomenal. General manager Fred Kroeger accepts the first of Allison's four "E" awards in 1943. Among distinguished Allison leaders at the ceremony were retired general manager and chief engineer Norman Gilman (front row, second from left) and works manager Bill Guthrie (second row, left).

climbs straight up to disappear in the blue sky above upturned faces. The genial informality of Colonel Jimmy Doolittle conversing casually with workers and secretaries. The deeply moving lobby display of a bullet-riddled V1710 engine returned home after bringing its pilot and plane safely back to base. The ceremony in March 1944 at which Ed Newill presented Army Air Force officers with the 50,000th V1710, and received in exchange "Old No. 9," the first V1710 to fly.

The "E" Award

In 1906 the United States Navy inaugurated a tradition of awarding an "E" for excellence to units that displayed exceptional loyalty, devotion, and service. After Pearl Harbor came the realization that the men and women of American industry were genuine partners with the fighting forces. So emerged the Army-Navy Production Award, a joint recognition by the Army and the Navy of exceptional performance and patriotism on the home front. Selection of recipients was made by the Boards for Production Awards and included the privilege of flying an Army-Navy "E" burgee above the plant for six months. Each employee received a silver "E" insignia pin.

Every six months following, production performance was reviewed to determine continuation of the honor. Service stars could be added to the burgee to acknowledge each half-year of continuing merit. Allison's first award came in October 1942, the second and third in 1944, and the fourth on April 21, 1945.

Continued on page 81

The V1710 at War

The Curtiss P-40—Warhawk, Tomahawk, and Kittyhawk

The P-40 and the V1710 were originally matched to accomplish a specific mission that fortunately never materialized: defensive war in North America. Strategists planning for such a contingency envisioned the U.S. having only one chance to repel invasion at unknown points along the eastern seaboard. That meant defensive pursuit planes rugged enough to survive in combat stationed at inland bases. The planes could be launched quickly with ammunition for low-level strafing and bombing and fuel to fly 700 miles or more.

After the XP-40's lively show at the delayed 1938 Pursuit Competition, the airplane served in every theatre of World War II, creating legends as she flew. From 1938 to 1944, the Curtiss-Wright Corporation built 17,738 P-40s in six principal variants for the air forces of the U.S., Britain, the Soviet Union, the Free French, and China's American Volunteer Group (AVG).

Among P-40 legends, none endures more vividly than U.S. Air Corps Major Claire Lee Chennault's AVG, the Flying Tigers, not least because of 150 or so V1710 engines unique among the 70,000 made. The AVG was formed in 1941 and comprised three squadrons trained in Burma under Chennault. One squadron went into action in China against the invading Japanese in December 1941, the others remained in Burma to reinforce the Royal Air Force.

The first Flying Tiger success came on December 20, 1941, when the group shot down six Mitsubishi bombers. Over all, the group recorded 286 confirmed victories with 12 pilots lost in action. Squadron Leader Robert

Claire Chennault's American Volunteer Group was created at the request of the Chinese government to help China defend herself from Japan. The AVG included the 3rd Pursuit Squadron—the "Hell's Angels"—stationed at Toungoo, Burma. The group's 72 pilots and ground personnel, c. 1941, were assigned 31 P-40s. Squadron Leader A.E. Olson stands sixth from left.

Far from headquarters, field maintenance is performed on a Curtiss P-40 early in WWII. Headlamps for lighting and 55-gallon drums for ladders were routine, but the hammer on the air intake probably wasn't. The Royal Australian Air Force truck and the aircraft's paint scheme suggest the South Pacific.

H. Neale scored 16 victories, Lt. Col. Gregory "Pappy" Boyington earned six and later accumulated 22 more to become the USMC's leading ace. The Tigers in 1942 were "regularized" as the USAAF 23rd Fighter Group.

The Matter of Interchangeability

In changing from Allison's original job shop system, in which each engine was built up one at a time, to the high volume production begun in 1939, component interchangeability became an important factor, from drawings to final assembly. Interchangeability was an inspection standard for the Army Air Corps inspectors assigned to accept engines for the government. Components were rejected for the most minute variation from dimensional standard.

During early production of C-model engines destined for British and American P-40s, the accumulated store of these rejected parts became the Flying Tigers' roar. When representatives of the Chinese government came to Indianapolis in late 1939 to order engines for their newly-purchased P-40s, Allison regretfully explained that every engine on the line was spoken for—by the British, the French, the U.S. Army Air Corps.

Then someone thought about the storeroom full of off-size parts. They weren't strictly interchangeable, but they were perfectly sound. Perhaps if they were matched and mated, they'd make up enough engines to meet the AVG order. The Chinese were delighted. Steel inserts were plated to fit oversize tapped holes, connecting rod bearings were altered to fit slightly undersize crankshafts, and dozens of other similar fixes were made. Some 150 engines were all hand-fitted by Allison people who had previously been engine builders for Duesenberg, Stutz, and Marmon. When tested, these units developed more horsepower and used less fuel than the regular engines which the U.S. military would accept.

"We loved to tell the story afterwards," said a retired engineer, "that in the field those engines made out of matched parts that had been rejected on Army standards had a better field record than the standard engines. We just loved to tell people that, and it was true."

Company Support for the AVG

Training director Pop Kreusser selected Tye M. Lett, Jr. and Arne Butteberg to direct the setup of maintenance operations for the AVG's engines in the field, and Chennault's crew chiefs and 11 Chinese-Americans with aeronautical experience spent up to six weeks training at Allison in Speedway. Lett and Butteberg left Indianapolis on May 12, 1941, and took Pan American's *California Clipper* on her maiden flight from San Francisco to Manila, then a Dutch steamer to Hong Kong. From there, a Chinese National Aeronautical Corporation DC-3 flew them to Burma via Chungking and Kunming.

Three Very Special Warhawks

During almost three decades at Allison, engineer Bill Thomas contributed to nearly all its engine programs, including the J71, T56, and TF41. His first Allison engine was the V1710 in the P-40, and he recalls their meeting vividly.

"In January 1939, after finishing two years of engineering at Rose-Hulman Institute, I joined the U.S. Army Air Corps to avoid being drafted into the Infantry. And I really loved airplanes. I was at Clark Field in the Philippines with the first B-17 squadron to ferry planes from Boeing Field across the Pacific.

"During the few months we fought in the Philippines, we lost our B-17s. In late December 1941 I moved 600 miles south to Delmonte on the Island of Mindanao. Twenty Air Corps engineering people, me included, were sent to the beach at a village named Bugo for different duty than we were used to.

"In early March 1942, the freighter *Western Farmer,* with a completely volunteer crew, arrived from Australia with three brand-new P-40 fighters lashed to the deck—the only Air Corps reinforcements to reach the Philippines before the fall of the islands. To prevent attack by Japanese aircraft, the ship was beached and the cargo brought ashore by a makeshift breeches buoy. Each airplane was packed in two large crates, one the fuselage with engine installed, the other the wing assembly. They were unloaded into a large coconut grove that stretched along the beach for several miles.

"We were to assemble these aircraft and to attempt to get them back to Delmonte—with few tools and no cranes or hoists. To raise the fuselage and engine components high enough to get the wing underneath and lower the gear, we commandeered a local lumber company's block-and-tackle rig that we slung in a coconut tree. Our experience was limited to air-cooled radial Wright and P&W engines. Our entire understanding of these in-line liquid-cooled engines was a study of the manuals, which luckily were included in the crates.

In the Philippines sometime in 1942, field assembly of P-40s was accomplished under somewhat more luxurious conditions than Bill Thomas found. The fuselage, with engine installed, is hoisted over the wing unit with the overhead pulley and lowered into place.

"The Allison link here is first that the manuals must have been well written indeed for a bunch of kids to understand and use successfully. Second, all three of these Allison V1710 engines had been manufactured in Indianapolis in mid-December, just a few days after Pearl Harbor. And here they were in the Philippines the following March.

"During the time we were assembling the planes, Japanese reconnaissance aircraft passed overhead often and at odd hours. After the first few scares we realized that they couldn't see us through the trees. As soon as we cut trees to allow pushing the planes the few hundred feet to the single-lane gravel road which paralleled the beach, the Japanese would probably spot us. So we waited until the night before we intended to fly the planes out. Then, with lots of help from the Filipinos, we cleared our 'taxiway.'

"Each day almost on schedule, a four-engine Japanese flying boat passed over right at noon, always coming from the same direction, and flying a straight line course. We called him Photo Charlie. Scheduled to fly the first plane out was our senior pilot, Lt. Warden. Even though we were ready at 10:30 a.m., he kept stalling and checking and waiting. We suspected that he was worried about flying off the narrow gravel road.

"Actually, he was waiting for something. He took off just before noon with no problem. Warden took off, turned out to sea, and disappeared. He hadn't been gone ten minutes when we heard the drone of Photo Charlie. We thought that if Warden had been just a bit later, he might have gone after him. Just as Charlie was overhead, we heard the high-pitched scream of a diving fighter, and out of the sun and firing came our P-40. His dive carried him under Charlie, and as he pulled up under him, Warden fired again. Charlie was burning and crashed in the mountains about 10 miles away. Next day our Filipino friends brought souvenirs from Charlie, whose meticulous timetable had cost the Japanese a large airplane and crew."

With Friends Like This

Bob Hoover, who in 1949 came to Allison's Flight Test operations, has a P-40 "combat" story with a twist:

"[While I was in flight training] during September 1942 in St. Petersburg, Florida, we lost a P-40 because of an engine problem, rumored to have been some sort of bearing, and a fellow had bailed out. Soon afterward six of us in a P-40 V-formation were diving on water slicks marked with irridescent dye for target practice. We had tracers to help us get the feel of the thing, and we went round in a rectangular pattern, then dove, shot, and pulled up. I was starting down on my run and had no more triggered my guns than suddenly my engine was on fire. "Oh, oh," I thought, "it's those bearings." So I pulled up but couldn't get high enough to bail out. So I opened up the canopy and headed for the beach and ditched it.

"My commanding officer landed on the beach in a little plane, maybe a Cub. A nearby fishing boat picked me up. The CO asked me what was wrong, and I said, 'Engine failure. It caught fire and I shut everything off and ditched.' The next day we returned, and in the shallow water we could see the ship sitting on the bottom. They fished it out and it was full of .50 calibre bullet holes. The fellow behind me was concentrating on the target and just didn't see me, and shot me full of holes."

With about 2,000 more airframes to come, the 15,000th P-40 Warhawk bears insignia of many U.S. and Allied air force units in which its sister ships served. The plane was photographed near the Curtiss-Wright plant in Buffalo, New York, in November 1944.

Lucky Lightning

Of all the Allison-powered aircraft of World War II, none was more glamorous nor more successful than Lockheed's P-38 Lightning. John Goldthwaite recalled a nervous afternoon when an early Lightning narrowly escaped possible disaster: "One of our first engines for the P-38 went through the full production run and somehow a faulty reduction gear pinion had been installed. After failure on the test stand, that reduction gear pinion was dead soft, worn halfway through, had somehow escaped the heat treatment. We had shipped two engines to Lockheed. So we stopped shipping them all right. We wired our representative at Lockheed and told him to hold up installation of that engine. We invented an excuse so they wouldn't fly it until we'd looked at this thing. Then we telephoned him at his hotel and said, 'Now, the real reason is, you take the cover off that gear box and take a file and find out if those gear teeth are hard, because we found one gear that hadn't been hardened. You can tell with a file,' we said. 'And you report back to us right away.' Well, it turned out it was all right, so he put the gear box back together and Lockheed flew it and it was successful, and that was the start of the P-38."

At the height of wartime output in 1943, Lockheed's Burbank, California, P-38 production line made an impressive sight. Almost 10,000 Lightnings were built by war's end, accounting for a substantial portion of Allison's V1710 installations.

The heavily-armed P-39 made an excellent ground support fighter particularly popular with the Russian Air Force to whom thousands were flown via Alaska and Siberia. Pilots grumbled about the plane's cold cockpit: instead of helping to warm toes and fingers, the rear-mounted engine's external heat was largely shed uselessly into the slipstream.

Bottom: The Bell P-39 Airacobra was designed for a rear-mounted engine. The long shafting was vibration-damped with a hydraulic unit. The engine location permitted installation of a .37mm cannon that fired through the prop hub. Maintenance under camouflage nets in the South Pacific was photographed early in WWII.

The Wonders of Shafting

Before World War II, the primary company objective was to do everything possible with the V1710 engine. Chief engineer Ron Hazen became famous for his willingness to take on challenging projects—shafting, turbosupercharging, most anything. Larry Bell's designers came up with the P-39 Airacobra, with engine behind the pilot, requiring a uniquely complex installation.

Engineer Bill Emmick tells this story: "The first engine test lasted ten minutes because of a shaft failure in the accessories housing due to severe torsional vibration in the shaft and engine combination. Design engineer Oscar Montieth and project manager Marshall Davis devised the first hydraulic dampener to handle the torsional vibration, and more than 7,000 P-39s were flown across the Arctic to Russia without a single failure of engine or shaft."

One of World War II's finest fighters, the North American Aviation P-51 Mustang was designed for Britain's Royal Air Force. Based upon requirements set by the British Purchasing Commission in New York early in 1940, NAA president James H. "Dutch" Kindleberger and his design team in Inglewood, California, began design for the new fighter. The plane, designated NA73, was planned for high volume manufacture from the outset. Its many advanced elements included a laminar-flow wing based on NACA studies.

The design was finished and a prototype built in an astonishing 78,000 engineering hours in 127 days. Fitted with its Allison V1710, the P-51A first flew October 26, 1940. It soon achieved 382 mph at 14,000 ft, equal to the British Spitfire. but at higher altitudes its performance was limited by its lack of high altitude supercharging. Early Allsion-powered Mustangs performed with outstanding success in ground attack and intruder roles in northwest Europe in 1942-1944. Equipped with Packard-built Rolls-Royce Merlin engines specifically designed for high altitude, subsequent P-51Bs earned distinction as long-range escorts for heavy bombers.

Continued from page 74

The Peacetime Challenge Looms

As the crisis of the war yielded to predictions of victory for the Allied cause, General Motors executives were planning for a peacetime future that was surely just ahead.

For the corporation, the shift from the operational distortions of wartime would almost certainly benefit from rising demand for GM's long-established consumer products, from automobiles to refrigerators, but at Allison Ed Newill could anticipate no such ready markets. The very existence of his division since 1932 was inextricably linked to military aviation. The division's production of 70,000 V1710s and 10 million aircraft engine bearings were impressive proof of what the firm could accomplish. But with the abrupt termination of high-volume military contracts only a matter of time, Norman Gilman's early determination to have a viable product took on still greater urgency—if Allison were to survive beyond its initial great successes.

History had several surprises in store for Edward Newill and his staff at Jim Allison's thriving but precariously positioned enterprise. Among them lay a photograph in a general's desk drawer at Wright Field in Dayton.

Later P-51s were fitted with Packard-built Rolls-Royce Merlin engines. A sophisticated Aeroproducts four-bladed prop helped to provide some of the ship's legendary performance. Aeroproducts test pilot Raleigh Martin takes a break at the company's hangar at Dayton Municipal Airport sometime late in the war.

CHAPTER 6
Transitioning

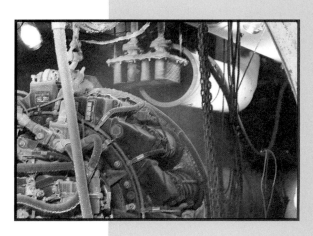

*Planning for peacetime.
From pistons to jets; V1710 yields to
J33 and J35; how to price a jet engine.
Whittle and GE. Jet manufacturing,
setting records. Development and
volume manufacture conflict, the
Allison/GM anomaly. Markets of
opportunity; transmissions, bearings,
locomotive parts, shock absorbers. The
automatic transmission comes to
Indianapolis.*

Previous page: Designated the XB-39, the Boeing B-29 Superfortress at the Fisher Body Division at Romulus Field in Cleveland, Ohio, in 1944 during installation of 2,600-hp V3420-A16 engines and special nacelles. In the background are Fisher P-75 fighters.

Director of engineering Ron Hazen (center) shares jet engine production information with two influential visitors in 1946. Charles Wilson (left), whose recommendations influenced GM's acquisition of Allison in 1929, was GM president from 1941 to 1953, when he was named Dwight Eisenhower's Secretary of Defense. Alfred P. Sloan, Jr., (right) was GM president from 1923 to 1937, and chairman of the board from 1937 to 1956.

Corporations are like complex living organisms, with distinctive characteristics, unique personalities. Their destinies are shaped by the people who lead them, by the forces of history, and even the whimsy of fate.

Allison is no exception. From the comparative spontaneity and flexibility of its early days, the company at the end of World War II found itself of a size and in a place not entirely of its own choosing. That situation would recur in the late 1970s, but at the end of WWII, Allison's leaders strove to rebalance the company and its resources to survive in a radically-changed environment.

A View from Detroit

The long-term strategy for each of its divisions received careful consideration from General Motors management. Allison's postwar adjustment was but one, if unique, among many challenges facing the corporation. GM had, after all, radically altered the shape and conduct of almost every facet of its operation to meet the wartime emergency. Observed GM chairman Alfred Sloan: "Only a small proportion of GM products have wartime applications. When we were mobilized during WWII, we were obliged to transform the great bulk of our operations almost completely, to learn rapidly and under great pressure how to produce tanks, machine guns, aircraft propellers, and many other kinds of equipment with which we had no experience at all." During the war, GM produced $12 billion worth of military goods, and between February 1942 and September 1945, built no passenger cars in the U.S.

Wartime GM Policy Making

Under chairman Sloan and president Charles E. "Engine Charley" Wilson, GM had devised a wartime decision-making structure that included a three-member Policy Committee (Wilson and executive vice presidents Bradley and Hunt) to handle all operations policies. The 14-member War Administration Committee directed all war operations for the duration.

In his 1942 report to the Postwar Planning Group that became the basis for GM's aviation program, Sloan called out three major markets: commercial air transport, private civilian flying, and the military. Even with great expansion of commercial flying, sales potential for a single aircraft manufacturer was likely to be limited, said the report; safety hazards then inherent in small planes would limit the private flying market as compared to the automobile; and the military market was seen as likely to be both limited and highly technical—and therefore expensive.

Allison and GM Aviation Prospects

In August 1943 the GM policy committee had concluded an analysis of the corporation's role in aviation with two policy decisions. First, the corporation should not produce complete airframes in either the military or transport areas. This thinking led GM to sell its interests in Bendix and North American in 1948. Second, the corporation "should develop as complete a position on the manufacture of accessories as its capacity and circumstances make possible."

Those decisions were consistent with Detroit's attitudes towards the Allison Division articulated by Sloan: "First, to manufacture complete airplanes would jeopardize the other aviation business of the corporation. The Allison Division was, and would continue to be, a major producer of airplane engines and aircraft accessories applicable with minor variations to many kinds of planes and might normally account for 40 percent of the cost of the complete airplane. Such a manufacturer would need the confidence of the aircraft manufacturers, not to be a competitor." And second, "We do research in our fields of competence, but we are largely a production organization."

The Allison Flexibility

During 1944 Ed Newill's concern for Allison's future took him frequently to Detroit for planning sessions with GM group vice president Bob Evans. Evans launched a survey of other divisions to assess the matching of their potential peacetime needs with the enormous manufacturing capacity soon to be freed at Allison. Among suitable prospects were shock absorbers for Delco, blowers for Detroit Diesel, and hydraulic lift pumps for International Harvester. Plant 3, the original Allison production plant, would be converted and tooled for the manufacture of these commercial products.

Grander tasks were in the making, but these options would serve as excellent interim products to maintain a core of fiscal stability. Not the least of those products were the gears, bearings, and other precision components that flowed north to a busy factory just outside Chicago.

The Railroad Coupling

Having laid the groundwork with substantial research and development work on diesel engines in the 1930s, General Motors assumed unchallenged postwar dominance in the massive switch of America's railroads from steam to diesel power. All across the land, the thunder and hiss of the iron horse yielded to the steady throb of powerful,

With many of their precision components built at Allison plants, GM's Electro-Motive Division diesel locomotives began to dominate American railroading immediately after WWII. During the 1950s the handsome E and F-series units, often painted in vivid liveries, headed most of the nation's passenger and freight trains. Striking in deep orange, forest green, and metallic gold striping, these 1,500-hp F-7 A and B passenger units were built at EMD's La Grange shops for Great Northern in 1952.

economical diesel locomotives. Most of the sleek and colorful new engines first saw daylight in La Grange, Illinois. They bore the stylish nameplate of the Electro-Motive Division of General Motors.

So highly regarded were EMD locomotives for their quality and performance, that leading railroad historian S. Kip Farrington wrote in 1949, "In fact, it is my opinion that there would be few other Diesels ordered than those produced by Electro-Motive if this concern could turn them out fast enough."

The Electro-Motive Engineering Corporation, incorporated in August 1922 in Cleveland, Ohio, was acquired by GM in 1930. The three million-square-foot La Grange factory was built in 1935, and most of the modern procedures and systems for mass production of standardized railway locomotives were pioneered there. Allison became a core supplier of major components, from bearings to gears, for the hundreds of locomotives that rolled ceaselessly from La Grange during the late 1940s and into the 1950s.

An Orderly Mess

Even with all this planning, the suddenness of the end of the war made an orderly transition to peacetime operations impossible. It took 9,000 freight carloads just to haul away GM's military inventory, another 8,000 to dispose of government equipment and machinery. "Meanwhile," wrote chairman Sloan, "we were rushing to equip our plants for commercial production. Altogether there was a mess but no confusion."

Values and Allison's Search for Direction

For Allison, of course, no loyal customers were flocking showrooms eager to snap up new models.

Among Ed Newill's special worries were the futures of Allison's 20,000 employees, for whom only about 4,600 jobs would be available by January 1946. Understandably, a high percentage of the peak work force were people eager to return to their pre-war occupations on the farms and in neighboring communities. But Allison was an important focus for many skilled and experienced employees, including a portion of the 3,538 Allison men who had been drafted into the armed services by December 1943.

In Indianapolis, Allison management choices dealt pragmatically and sensibly with immediate problems and short-term solutions, but always with an eye to the big opportunity if and when it might develop. In fact, the aggregate wisdom of many relatively small decisions would facilitate not simply survival but considerable prosperity. Along with common sense, key elements of Allison's success after 1945 continued to be sound engineering, a willingness to tackle unusual technical problems, devotion to quality, and a consistent commitment to seeing a project through to user satisfaction that was not lost in the marketplace. On more than one occasion, the well-earned Allison reputation for integrity would help to buoy the company through difficulties.

An Interruption

In April 1945 when the Army Air Forces terminated Allison's V1710 volume production, the company was forced to lay off all but 2,600 bargaining unit employees. On November 19, 1945, the local, along with locals in other GM plants across the nation struck to regain wages lost as a result of wartime freezes. The union calculated that its members were an average of 30 cents per hour behind on wages.

The strike continued until March 23, 1946, and among the settlement offer conditions were an 18.5-cent-per-hour increase and some additional fringe benefits. During the early phase of the stoppage, management moved key administrative offices into a downtown hotel. Bargaining unit employees refused to enter the plants, of course, and salaried employees were shut out, except for the Protection Service staff.

Railway and Teamster unions supported the strike, refusing to deliver shipments. In December a court injunction allowed salary workers back into the plants. In an unanticipated side effect of the stoppage, more than a few managers and engineers reported that enforced time away from pressures of that turbulent time provided welcome opportunities to concentrate on technical and managerial innovations.

No Reasonable Offer Refused

While Newill shored up Allison with his network of supplementary production for other divisions, and undertook the launch of commercial and military transmissions, the aviation people were not diverted from their true calling. No success came easily. Allison aero engineers and managers went through dozens of prototypes for each winning product or installation.

Until 1946 when Ralph Golt and Bill Gage put together the nucleus of a sales department to solicit commercial applications, the installation engineers took the company's wares to the customer, whether military or airframe builders. "We were half salesman, half engineer," recalled James E. "Jim" Knott (who would become Allison general manager and a GM vice president). Taking the initiative was a major Allison tactic. "We often would design an unsolicited installation for a particular airframe and take it to the builder to inspire them. Harry Karcher (later to lead major Allison projects) and I in Indianapolis would assemble some hypothetical designs from our stable of components for an appealing airplane, then I'd take them out to companies and say, 'Here's what you can do.'"

Displayed in February 1946 at Northwest Airlines' Michigan Avenue ticket office in Chicago, the XB-42 propulsion layout shows the large gearbox that permitted independent prop operation. To the left can be seen a drawing of a proposed Douglas passenger plane application of the drive scheme—the original DC-4—that was not pursued. The Mixmaster Rockettes are Northwest staffers.

Two 1,425-hp V1710-E23Bs, located in the top of the fuselage and connected to the remote gearbox with 30-foot drive shafts, drove pusher-type, counter-rotating props in the tail cone of the 1945 Douglas XB-42 Mixmaster light bomber.. The advent of jet engines terminated the project.

In 1945 the Fisher Aircraft Development activity was closed and several engineers transferred to Allison to form the Installation Engineering Section whose objective was to sell engines for commercial applications. Said Knott, "We studied adaptations of 1710 engines, and later turbines, to almost every commercial aircraft then being considered."

Projects that did not see production included the Douglas B-42 in which two V1710 engines mounted in the fuselage drove counter-rotating propellers in the tail through 27 feet of shafting. Inevitably nicknamed the Mixmaster, the XB-42 used fail-safe gearing so that counter-rotation was maintained even with one engine out. Under chief engineer Ed Burton, the Douglas design staff also projected an enlarged version of the B-42 as a commercial transport—the original DC-4 design idea—but airline buyers resisted both the unconventional layout and the liquid-cooled engines. The airlines were no more receptive to the idea of V1710s for the Douglas DC-6, for which Don Berlin prepared a complete nacelle design.

An opportunity to reengine Boeing's B-17 Flying Fortress with the F series V1710 engines was lost in Southern California's Tehachapi mountains. In 1943 Air Force General Don Putt was concerned to improve the B-17's performance and to provide an alternative in case of shortages of its Wright R-1820 radial engines. At Putt's suggestion, Lockheed's Vega division, which had manufactured nearly 3,000 Flying Fortresses under license in Burbank, designed a V1710 nacelle for a B-17 test airplane, the XB-38. During May tests the plane verified the expected performance improvements. But on a flight over Bakersfield a fire developed, the crew abandoned ship, and the prototype crashed.

Another attempt came, this time to fit the V3420 to Boeing's B-29 Superfortress, designated the XB-39. Don Berlin, whose first Allison collaboration was as Curtiss' chief P-40 designer, and who had designed

Engineer Don Berlin, who had been Curtiss' chief designer for the P-40 before coming to Indianapolis to head up Allison flight test operations, led such programs as the V3420 nacelle for the XB-39 and the proposed V1710 installation for the Douglas DC-6 passenger liner.

In May 1943 an experimental installation of 1,425-hp V1710-F17 engines was made in a Boeing B-17E Flying Fortress. Performance of the resulting XB-38 was superior to the radial engine plane, but interrupting Boeing's production to tool up for a new variant was determined to be excessively time-consuming.

Above: T he XB-39, A Boeing B-29 Superfortress airframe, makes an early test flight with her V3420s newly-installed in winter 1944-45.

Center, right: Allison's chief test pilot for many years, B.T. "Red" Hulse prepares for a test flight during 1945 in a Fisher XP-75, whose counter-rotating Aeroproducts propellers were driven by the Allison V3240 engine.

Facing, bottom: In 1939 Douglas built the 160,000-lb XB-19, the world's largest land plane, with a wing span of 212 ft. The plane was used as a flying laboratory, and among her assignments was testing of Allison V3420 nacelles for the XB-39 in 1944.

the XB-19A installation and the Fisher XP-75, came from GM's Detroit Aircraft Development section to head the installation department at Allison's Plant 10 assisted by Bill Watson. Jim Knott was assigned to Berlin's group as chief powerplant engineer and supervised design and construction of the XB-39 nacelle in the GM Styling Section building on Milwaukee Avenue.

Like Riding a Bicycle

The XB-39 nacelle was first flight-tested, on the Douglas XB-19A testbed airplane, in December 1944. The flight was memorable on several counts, not the least of which was its unorthodox crew. Recalled

Knott, "I remember that flight very well because on that day the assigned flight engineer had come down with the flu, and Colonel Ernie Warburton, the Army Air Force test pilot, was going to postpone the flight. I brashly announced that I had been a flight engineer on Pan American's Boeing 314 flying boats, and had worked on the installation of these engines. Since I knew the controls and systems well, I could fly as flight engineer. Of course I was thrilled, but when Allison and GM learned of my volunteering, they promptly grounded me, saying that they hadn't hired me to do experimental flight testing." The project, too, was grounded as the war drew to a close.

The Douglas XB-19, then the largest bomber in the world, was characterized by engineer Al Sobey as "an overgrown, four-engine DC-3 with a span over 200 feet. The wings were so thick that I could crawl out to read the instruments mounted behind the outboard engines."

The Turbine Touchstone

Even while Allison bent its every energy during WWII to building V1710s and planned when it could for peacetime, once again an engine designed under the pressures of world war was being readied for history and a significant role in the Allison story.

Soon after the U.S. entered the war, epochal advances in turbine technology in Germany, Italy, and England became cause for real concern to American military leaders, particularly Deputy Chief of Staff for Air, General Henry H. "Hap" Arnold. On February 25, 1941, Arnold asked National Advisory Committee for Aeronautics chairman Vannevar Bush to appoint a special committee on jet propulsion whose purpose would be to coordinate early U.S. acquisition of jet engine capabilities.

In March the group was named. It was headed by Will Durand, with representatives from the Army Air Forces, the National Bureau of Standards, Johns Hopkins University, Massachusetts Institute of Technology, and three firms with reputations in steam and gas turbine

Famed for his farsighted vision and called by some "the father of the U.S. Air Force," Gen. Hap Arnold no sooner learned of Frank Whittle's revolutionary jet engine in 1941 than he acted decisively to acquire its technology for the U.S. With a P-38 behind them, Arnold confers with Lockheed Aircraft Corporation president Robert Gross and an aide in Burbank in November 1944.

work—Allis Chalmers, General Electric, and Westinghouse. GE was particularly respected by the military because of its leadership, dating to World War I, in turbosupercharger development. Arnold specifically excluded the major manufacturers of reciprocating engines—Allison, Pratt & Whitney, and Curtiss-Wright—because the three firms were fully occupied with wartime production of reciprocating engines.

Frank Whittle's Engine

In Britain, Frank Whittle's W-1X centrifugal compressor jet engine had first run in December 1940 and flew, in the Gloster E.28/39, on May 15, 1941. Arnold was invited by the British Air Ministry to observe the Gloster perform a few days later. He returned to Washington determined to get a U.S. jet engine moving with no further delay. He asked GE engineering vice president R.C. Muir to confer with the military to review the British engine project under terms of an agreement signed by U.S. Secretary of War Henry Stimson and Sir Henry Self of the British Air Commission, by which the Whittle technology would be made available on condition of rigorous secrecy.

Arnold and senior Army Air Force officers met with four General Electric managers and worked out an agreement under which GE would build 15 of the Whittle engines. Larry Bell, president of Bell Aircraft in Buffalo, New York, was informed the next day that his company was to build an airframe for the new engine.

The British Are Coming

The British drawings that arrived at GE's River Works in Lynn, Massachusetts, proved a bit cryptic and incomplete in some areas. The British obliged by sending a sample engine and three technicians to aid the GE engineers. On April 18, 1942, GE's Type I-A (pronounced "eye"-A) engine ran successfully. Whittle himself came to the U.S. (staying in Boston under an assumed name) in June 1942 to provide advice and counsel as the engine was being readied for installation in the Bell airplane. On October 2, 1942, Bell's XP-59A Airacomet, piloted by Bell's Bob Stanley, at Muroc Dry Lake, California, made America's first jet-powered flight.

Yes, But What Is it?

Several Allison episodes have, with the years, assumed mythic status, to recur in the archives, in the memories of participants, and as hearsay with remarkable consistency. Such a tale is that of Allison's introduction to Whittle's invention. The classic version follows:

"In June 1944 Ed Newill was visiting Wright Field, home of the Air Materiel Command. Allison had just finished its 50,000th V1710, and government funding for new Allison test flight facilities at Plant 10 had been approved. D-Day was in the papers. Walking down the hall, Allison's general manager heard: 'Mr. Newill, will you step in here a minute?' From a desk drawer, a senior procurement man took a photo. 'Can you make this for us?' 'Aircraft engines are our business,' replied Newill looking at the photographs, 'If that's what you want, we will make them. It is a jet engine, isn't it?' 'Yes, and we would like to have your firm price and production schedule in one week.'

"'That's not much time,' replied Newill. 'I know, but we need these in the worst sort of way.' 'Can we have a model and prints shipped to Allison?' 'There is no model,' interrupted the procurement man. 'A set of prints?' 'The blueprints are not complete as the design is not finished.'

"'Can I have a picture? Dimensions? Weight?' 'That is about all that I can give you.' With that skimpy information, Newill came home with 'one week' still in his ears. Newill called his staff together and repeated the request. With the meager information in hand, a detailed study was clearly impossible. After lengthy discussion, someone said: 'If we know how much it weighs, let's take the cost per pound of our present engine and apply that to the weight of the new engine, and give them that as the price.' No one had a better idea.

"A week later Newill returned to Wright Field with a firm price quote and a delivery schedule. Allison got the order and delivered its first engine on schedule within 10 percent of the original price quotation."

This Is What It Is

No one at Allison had anything beyond theoretical knowledge of the principles of jet propulsion in 1944, but they learned quickly in spite of secrecy precautions that were occasionally vexing.

Sworn to silence, a small group of engineers and manufacturing technicians visited the General Electric plant in Lynn. Among the group was John Goldthwaite, who recalled GE's superb cooperation warmly and the secrecy wryly: "Building 29 was the holy of holies of the project, so secret that my pass didn't even carry the name of the building. The GE people told me that they had trouble getting started because when the drawings first came over, nobody was authorized to open the three

In its earliest practical form, the turbojet employed a single centrifugal compressor that required the large circumference displayed by this early Allison production model J33 shown around 1945. Air intake is from the left end through the compressor; fuel (kerosene) was injected into the gas stream where it was ignited in the combustion chambers that angle in to the turbine stages, and then to the exhaust.

While an engineer trims a securing wire, several features of this early J33 can be seen, including the front mounting of accessories on the "W" support structure. Through the screened air inlets at the left, the front of the compressor guide vanes are visible.

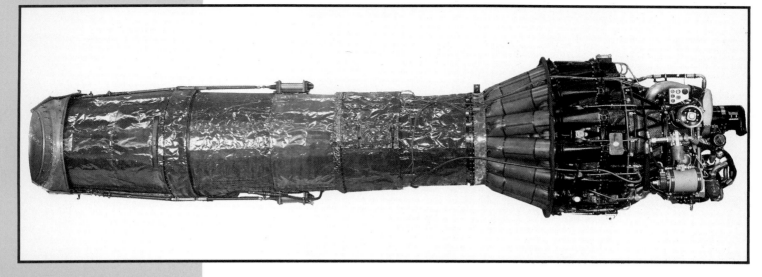

Viewed from the right side is the first of the production afterburning jets, the J33-A-33 of 1947. The afterburner, fitted in the turbojet's tailpipe, permits injection of additional fuel into the gas stream where its ignition provides increased thrust. This unit was used for the engine's 150-hour test.

In this 1947 production view with the engine vertically suspended nose down in the assembly stand, the J33 combustion chambers ("burner cans") and the first-stage turbine wheel blades (sometimes called "buckets") can be seen at the top. Vertical assembly helped to assure stability in rotating components and provided better lighting and access during manufacture.

seals—separate ones for the Army, the Navy, and the State Department. The State Department couldn't break Army or Navy seals, and neither the Army nor the Navy could break the State Department seal. They actually had to send those drawings back and get another set with only one seal before they were able even to see the drawings."

Back in Maywood, things went more smoothly. A study group of about 20 technicians, tooling men mostly, and one engineer met in a locked room upstairs in Plant 5. They studied the project to decide what had to be done, what tools had to be bought, and what procedures had to be followed to build the engine. The materials were specified on the drawings—but in GE numbers that had to be translated for interpretation. Continued Goldthwaite, "We were strictly forbidden to make any changes. Our engine had to be completely interchangeable with the GE at first, and they retained complete design responsibility. Any modification we wanted to make we had to clear through the General Electric plant at Lynn. And in turn, they had to clear through General Electric top headquarters at Schenectady."

The project at first included two basic engines, both centrifugal flow—the original I-16 (derived from the Whittle design) which generated 1,600 lbs of thrust, and the GE-designed, 4,000-lb-thrust I-40 (based on knowledge derived from Whittle's work) that became the J33. Allison had originally been invited into the jet engine business as a

manufacturing organization, not as a design or development group, because of the Army Air Force's anticipation of urgent war production requirements for the new engine type. Inevitably, the Allison team incorporated a growing number of design improvements into production engines, and as the I-40 matured into the J33, Allison ultimately manufactured 15,525, primarily for Lockheed's F-80, F-94 and T-33; Grumman's F9F; Chance Vought's Regulus missile; and Martin's B-61 Matador. The first Allison J33 was delivered February 3, 1945.

The next phase of U.S. turbine engine development came with GE's introduction of the axial-flow TG-100/T31 engine in the 4,000-lb-thrust class. The Air Force chose to fund continued development and production of both engines. General Motors was asked to take on production responsibilities for the TG-100/T31, now designated the J35, as well.

Another Kelley Johnson airplane, Lockheed's F-80 Shooting Star carried the jet engine from exotic breakthrough into day-after-day practicality, setting records on the way. As America's first operational jet fighter, Allison-powered F-80s dominated Korean skies during the early days of the Korean War. In a dual-seat arrangement, the airframe later became the T-33 trainer in which an entire generation of USAF pilots entered the jet age.

Some of the Allison godfathers who nurtured the J33 into production, from left are T.S. McCrae, J.B. Wheatley, Fred Luker, Charlie McDowall, A.W.F. Green, W.C. Oestrike, J.C. Fetters, and R.P. Atkinson.

In December 1946 Allison built its first J35 jet engine, and its slender profile reveals the new compressor arrangement that has been standard for jet engine cores since. The more efficient axial layout allowed engine and plane designers greater flexibility of engine performance and installation options.

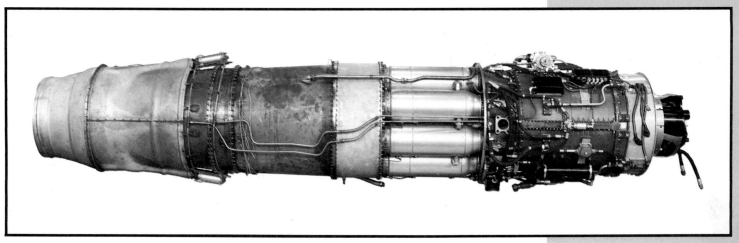

Testing of rotating parts was vital to jet engine development, particularly for compressor and turbine wheels with their complex castings. Turbine wheels were subject to both high rotation speeds and temperatures that significantly affected their metallic structure. A J33 compressor wheel is lowered into a sub-floor spin chamber for test. High-pressure steam provided the immensely high rotation speeds.

The first J35 was flight tested in February 1946—in a Republic XP-84. Because Allison itself was seen as fully involved in the J33, volume J35 production was assigned to Chevrolet's Tonawanda, New York, factory.

In 1947, as Chevrolet resumed full-scale auto production, J35 production was moved to Indianapolis, where Allison's growing expertise with turbine technology and available production capacity made an excellent match. General Electric, meanwhile, was developing the J47, and in the absence of Air Force direction of manufacturing resources, GE and Allison ceased their technology exchange and assumed the traditional roles of commercial competitors.

The New Turbine Universe

For Allison's aviation people, the new jets brought the sort of technical challenge on which they thrived. The J33 turbine wheel, for example, required a particularly hard steel that had to be machined on both sides in a very large lathe recalling the pre-production days of the V1710.

Perhaps the most severe problem, John Goldthwaite reported, was "the turbine wheels which ran practically red hot on the rim and at very high speed. Now and then a wheel would blow up on the test stand. We gathered up the pieces and tried to find the flaw, but we couldn't. GE was having the same problem. Our chief metallurgist, Arthur Green, finally made a metallurgical study with a history of every single forging including the particular mold at the steel mill, the particular ingot that was involved, and the particular position in the billet—the preliminary forging made from an ingot cast right out of the furnace. We found out that every broken wheel had come from the bottom of the ingot even after trimming of the accepted 20%. After they cut about 10 percent more off the bottom of the ingot, there never was a broken wheel."

An Occasional Chuckle

While Allison and GE mastered the manufacture of the new engines, jet aircraft began to make their way in the world. Early flights of Bell's XP-59 jet were all made in great secrecy. Even though he was working closely with both Bell and Curtiss in Buffalo at the time, Jim Knott knew nothing about the jet flights. But it wasn't long before the airplane drew public notice, reported Knott. "The airplanes were flown out of Niagara Falls and the test pilot was Jack Woolams, who soon found out that no one had ever seen an airplane flying without a propeller. The test flight area was adjacent to American Airlines' DC-3 flight path from Buffalo to New York. So Jack got a tall opera hat and a curved pipe. He'd put the hat on and the pipe in his mouth and fly up alongside the DC-3 and very slowly pass on by. Soon stories appeared in the local press describing a pilot with top hat, curved pipe and a propellerless plane."

From Oddity to Workhorse

In early 1946, jet engine time between overhaul (TBO) was set at 50 hours. Few operated that long, but by year end, the J33 achieved 100 hours TBO. Confidence in jet engines grew among designers, builders, pilots, and maintenance men. Early in 1947, water-alcohol injection gave the J33 additional power for takeoff. The J35 went into production at Allison rated at 4,000 pounds thrust. In May 1947 the J33 completed the first turbine engine 150-hour qualification test ever, meeting the same standard of dependability then demanded of reciprocating engines. Turbine engines had come of age.

Whether at 40,000 feet or on the ramp in Alaska, Air Force jets must perform well at low temperatures. Allison's cold chamber test cell provided the opportunity to see that they would. A J33 is prepared for a run.

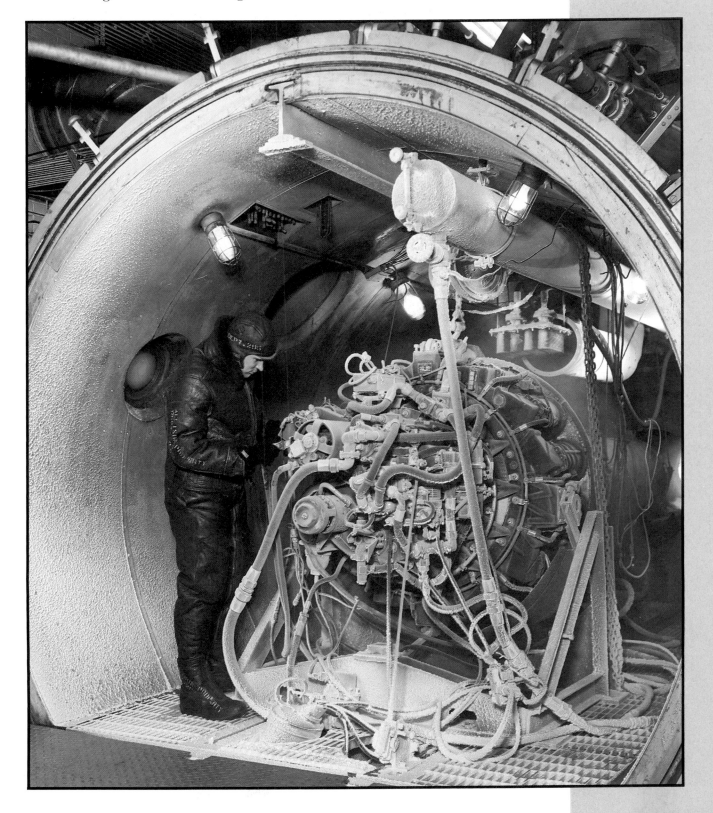

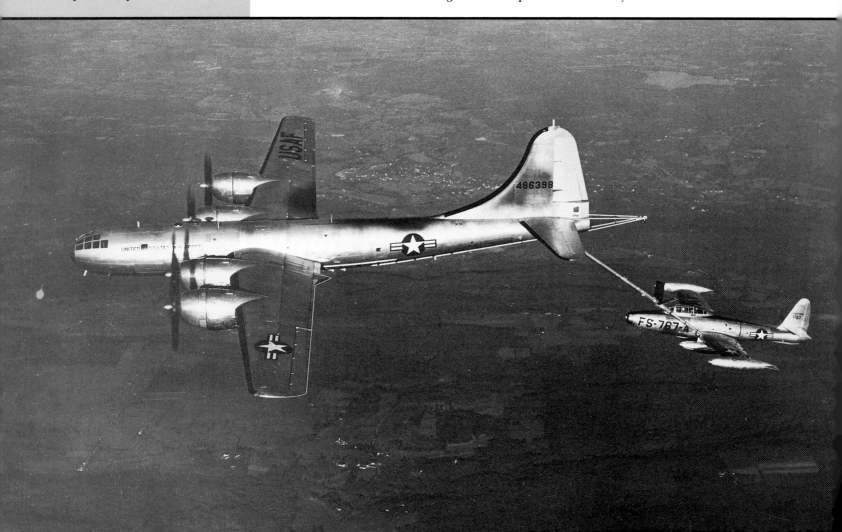

One of the J35's important installations was in the Republic F-84 Thunderjet. Equipped for mid-air refueling, fleets of F-84s made transoceanic delivery flights to overseas air bases across both the Atlantic and Pacific from 1950. An F-84G is refueled from a converted Boeing B-29 in the spring of 1952. The long overwater flights helped verify the jet engine's growing dependability.

Next, the Record Book

For more than 20 years the world speed record for straight-away flight had been kept in Europe, but Kelly Johnson's F-80 Shooting Star and its Allison J33 were about to make history. Lockheed turned over a production airplane to the Fight Test Base at Muroc Dry Lake, and on June 19, 1947, the F-80R streaked across the measured course for the new world speed mark of 623.8 mph.

A few weeks later an Allison J35 teamed with a Douglas D-558 Skystreak to achieve 640.7 mph, and five days later, 650.6 mph. Impressive statistics accumulated to validate both the technology and Allison's production mastery of the jet engine. In May, 1946, 25 J33-powered F-80s flew en masse from March Field, California, to Washington, D.C.—the first mass jet flight in history.

In July, 1948, 15 J33-powered F-80s made the first mass jet flight across the Atlantic Ocean from Selfridge Air Force Base to Dow Field through Greenland, Iceland, Scotland, England, and on to Furstenfeldbruck, Germany. The J33 also powered the first flight of a U.S. jet missile, the Martin Matador.

The Type Certificate

In early 1948 the J33-23 came into production. In April, the first Air Force group to be equipped with the J35-powered Republic F-84 Thunderjets was activated. In May the first jet engine approved for commercial use—the J33 developed and built by Allison—obtained CAA

approval, its
ATC type-
certificate.

In fall 1948 a Northrop YB-49 Flying Wing
powered by eight J35 engines flew nonstop more than 3,400
miles for a new distance record for jet aircraft, at an average
speed of 382 mph. By 1949, Allison had begun development of a new
high thrust engine, the J71. That same year marked Allison's delivery of
its 5,000th jet engine to U.S. Air Force. Through redesign and
production economies, the cost of J33 and J35 engines continued to
shrink. The original price of $55,000 for the J33 was down to less than
$20,000 by 1947 and the J35 which had started at $44,000 was at $36,900
in 1949.

The V1710 Last Hurrah

Allison met the final requirement for V1710 engines by producing 750
engines for the North American F-82 Twin Mustang, the last Air Force
fighter to be powered with reciprocating engines. With the conclusion of
that contract in December 1947, all further reciprocating engine
development was halted.

The First Allison Transmissions

Allison's steady progress in the air was matched by parallel
developments on the ground, and even before Pearl Harbor, the
foundation for what would ultimately become another Allison division
was being laid in Detroit.

In response to a request from the Army Ordnance Department for an
improved battle tank transmission, the first Torqmatic crossdrive
transmission had been conceived in 1941 by GM Product Study Group
Number 3 under engineering vice president Ormand Hunt and headed
by Oliver Kelley. The unit, designed for engine input of 850 hp, coupled
a torque converter to a powershift three-speed and reverse
transmission—technology completely new to heavy vehicle operation.
After extensive continued development to incorporate provisions for
vehicle steering and braking, and simple operator controls, by 1944 the
revolutionary CD-850 was ready for pilot testing.

Late that year, Allison managers, including chief designer Charlie
McDowall, met with Kelley and his group to explore Allison involvement
in refinement and manufacture of the unit. The project looked attractive
to everybody. In November GM group vice president Bob Evans and
Allison general manager Ed Newill proposed the new transmission to the
Army with the understanding that Allison would be the prime contractor.
The proposal was accepted, and in February 1945 the "B96 Transmission
Engineering Section" was established in Indianapolis within the Aircraft
Engineering Department. The embryo staff included engineers

*Two of Northrop's fifteen
172-ft-span XB-35 propeller-
driven Flying Wing strategic
bombers were converted to
YB-49 configuration with
eight J35 engines during
1947. Shown during a 1948
test flight at Edwards AFB,
California, is the No. One
YB-49. The ship was
destroyed on March 15,
1950, when the nose gear
collapsed and the ship
flipped over during a high-
speed taxi run. No one was
hurt in the incident.*

John Storer, U.A. Breting, P.B. Pritchard, and T. Bertrand; a secretary, and a single clerk.

The First Commercial Transmissions

As the end of the war approached, Robert M. Schaefer, a transmission and power train development engineer with GM's Detroit Transmission Division, submitted a proposal to his division general manager, V.A. Olsen, suggesting a series of Torqmatic transmissions to correspond with the Detroit Diesel Engine Division's line of engines for use in trucks, tractors, road machinery, boats, and off-highway applications. Olsen, an ex-Cadillac executive facing enormous demand for Hydramatic transmissions that completely filled capacity of his available plant, passed the proposal along to Bob Evans, group executive of the GM engine divisions. In Schaefer's proposal Evans saw the makings of an attractive match with the military transmission project already underway with Allison. GM's work with the Ordnance Department on cross-drives looked promising indeed, and the whole universe of heavy commercial vehicles had begun to seem like fertile ground for new transmission technology. Substantial production capability remained at the Allison Division in Indianapolis even with jet engine development and component production for other divisions.

After reviewing Schaefer's proposal, Evans wasted no time in asking the creative engineer to visit. "Schaefer, this is exactly what I want and I want you to get it for me." Evans had Schaefer transferred to Detroit Diesel with instructions to start a product study group for transmissions under Larry Sheldrick, director of engineering there. Evans chose marine gears as the first target market, and the first powershift marine gear was designed and pilot units fabricated there. The production responsibility was assigned to Allison, and Schaefer was transferred to Allison in September 1946.

Allison chief engineer Ron Hazen had already expanded the transmission section in April, naming Roy Lynch as chief engineer and Storer assistant chief for ordnance projects. Schaefer's new commercial projects made a perfect addition.

Parallel Division Components

In 1946 the Allison Division was divided into two separate operations under general manager Ed Newill. With reasonably-defined goals for Aircraft Operations and Transmission Operations, Allison was poised for the next stage of its development.

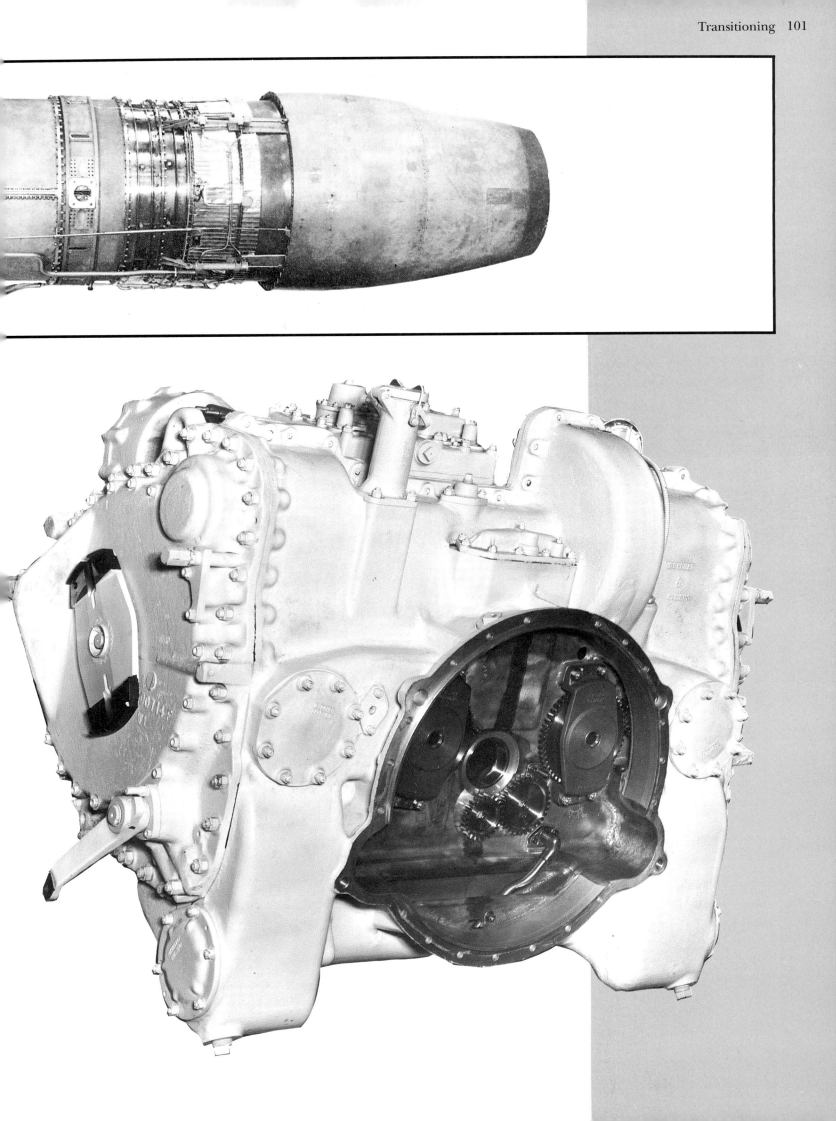

CHAPTER 7

Diversifying

Jet engines at war in Korea.
A turboprop dynasty begins with the
T40; Convair and Lockheed,
Tradewinds and Pogos.
Flight testing at Plant 10; the five-
engine Flying Fortress, the Hercules,
and the T56.
The Test Cell Explosion.
Approaching the Commercial Market.
Turbo-Liner, Hourglass, Convair 580;
Aeroproducts Propellers.
The jet engine comes of age.

Following the invasion of South Korea by Communist forces of North Korea, from July 1950 to July 1953 under the United Nations flag the United States fought one of the most grim wars in its history.

Moreover, as they had a decade earlier, engines from Indianapolis contributed mightily to victory.

Early in the war an aerial confrontation between a flight of North American P-51 Mustangs and Soviet Mikoyan-Gurevich MiG-15 jets (which had first flown in 1947) established the superiority of the jet airplane over the best of its piston predecessors.

As the nation's first volume builder of jet engines (J33 and J35 manufacturing had been concentrated in Indianapolis soon after their joint development with General Electric), Allison played a central role in the U.S. race to re-equip the Air Force with turbine power. Lockheed's F-80 and T-33 and Grumman's F9F-7 Cougar flew with J33s. The J35 powered the Republic F-84 Thunderjet, the Northrop F-89 Scorpion, and the Chance-Vought F7U-3 Cutlass. Among J71-powered aircraft was the Navy's McDonnell F3H Demon.

In November 1950 USAF Lt. Russell J. Brown, piloting an F-80C, downed the first enemy MiG-15 in warfare's first all-jet aerial combat. Within four months of the war's start, F-80s flew 15,500 sorties with 42 losses. Air Force records show that Allison engines powered 69 percent of all the conflict's jet fighter missions.

Beginning The Turboprop Connection

The company's work in refining the design of the J33s and J35s into increasingly powerful and reliable engines, then manufacturing them in high volume in time of national need, helped to carry Allison through a difficult transition. It further enhanced the company's reputation for capable performance.

However, in more important ways it was not the tens of thousands of J33s and J35s that carried the true Allison creative bloodline from the V1710, but a mere 240 or so T40 engines. For the T40—an unwieldy prodigy bursting with tough problems—represented a major, original creative work. It was a composite of innovation and devotion achieved in Speedway and Maywood—a genuinely Allison engine.

Bob Hicks, who retired in 1983 after 37 years with the company, characterized the pioneering work involved with Allison's first turboprop.

"The T40 was a complex machine, including 14-foot dual-rotation propellers, two power sections, remote mounting of the power sections from the reduction gear, clutches, and all sorts of hardware. It was among the most difficult aircraft engines to design and develop ever undertaken. Partly because of its complexity and partly because of inexperience in the industry at the time, the T40 never was very successful, but it did make some noteworthy achievements. Not the least of those

Northrop's F-89 all-weather interceptor was founder Jack Northrop's final major design. Named by Muroc AFB (later Edwards) crews for its slender, upswept tail, the Scorpion was powered by twin 7,200-lb.-thrust Allison J35s. More than 1,000 were built between 1948 and the late 1950s. At production peak, Ontario Airport in California was used as a pre-delivery staging area.

No powerplant in company history has taught Allison engineers more than the 2,890-lb T40 "monstrosity." Design was begun in 1945, and its dual power section, double gearbox, shafting, and decoupler mechanism, among other elements, provided crucial data for the T56/501 engine family. The T40 powered Convair's experimental seaplanes and the VTOL ships of the early 1950s, and the Douglas A2D Skyshark.

was preparation for the T56, among the company's—indeed the industry's—grand successes in performance and cost, the number produced, its worldwide usage."

A Design, A Contract, A Path

Although contract documents with the U.S. Navy for development of the big turboprop engine were not signed until June 1946, much of the T40's preliminary design work was accomplished during the 1945-46 union strike by engineer Art Gaubatz and aerodynamicist O.P. Pracher.

As crucial as its technical challenge, believes Jim Knott, was the product direction that the T40 established for Allison for decades: "The Navy put us into the turboprop business with their request for the T38 power section that became the T40. Yes, we said, of course we'd like to do that. But it sealed our fate, detracted from our interest in the pure jet business. We carved a niche for ourselves, but [the focus on turboprop technology] relegated us to third place in terms of gross sales [behind General Electric and Pratt & Whitney]."

Taming Twin Tornados

The T40 engine could best be described as a 5,500-hp monstrosity, a mechanical nightmare. The engineers loved it for those very reasons.

The gearbox also proved to be exciting. Allison was in the throes of developing the turboprop concept, and began probably 20 years ahead of where it should have been. Part of the challenge lay in the counter-rotating, dual power-section, 7,000-hp T40 gearbox engine for the vertical takeoff and landing (VTOL) airplanes then being developed at Convair and Lockheed.

Extrapolating from limited mechanical data and running at temperatures and gear speeds simply unheard of, the engineering staff ran tests to discover entire new regimes of phenomena and data.

The proportions of its 5,500-hp twin power section and dual propellers stand out on an early T40 engine in the calm of the Indianapolis test cell. To come are the perils of the installed environment —salt deposits, vibrating shafts, spawning fishes in the exhaust glow, and vanishing propellers.

The real
secret to
turboprops and
gear boxes lay in the
vibration questions: it was
necessary to explore all the
frequencies in the gearbox, then design each gear so it would not see
those frequencies. To measure vibration in the region of the new speeds
and meshing frequencies meant developing new tools, and much
innovation. Damper rings and pre-loaded bearings, for example, came
from extensive trial and error. Allison, observed engineers on the T40,
pretty much threw away the textbooks.

In the process, the excessive complexities of the T40 were eliminated in
favor of its basic strengths. The company then concentrated on what
became the T56—a single power section driving into a gearbox with no
clutches, a propshaft, a single propeller. But the T40 learning process
was rich with incident.

In June 1948 the Navy announced that the Convair XP5Y flying boat
would be powered by Allison turbo-prop engines, the first public
disclosure of the T40.

Jim Holman, whose career before joining Aeroproducts included many
years with Convair, met the T40 on that first installation, and observed
that the airplane itself posed tough problems. "The ramp team—Convair
engineering, Allison, and Aeroproducts people—came across with the
changes that took us from an engine unable to get off the ground to the
point where the -5Y made a 40-hour endurance flight at tremendous
speeds: the 2,890-pound engine produced 5,850 hp, more power at
takeoff than any engine then developed, and drove the 86-ton boat over
400 mph, pretty fast in those days, and met Navy requirements on many

This 17-ft-diameter tunnel was converted in 1951 from an old V1710 test stand in Plant 2 for testing of the T40 power package for VTOL aircraft. The 36-ton tunnel, mounted on two large bearings, could be rotated from horizontal to vertical. Exhaust was carried away through retractable, water-cooled pipes, and television observation cameras solved visibility limitations. Test technician Steve Stephanidis prepares a T40 for a run.

From the proud lineage of its WWII PBY Catalinas, Convair hoped to continue that success with turbine-powered seaplanes for cargo, reconnaissance, and other assignments. The 60-ton XP5Y-1 took shape in San Diego, California, on a 1948 Navy contract, and first flew in April 1950. Four 5,850-hp T40s drove 15-ft. counter-rotating Aeroproducts propellers. The ship was launched into the bay from huge submersible dollies.

technical issues. [But] in fact, the aircraft was unstable and they lost it to a buildup of uncontrollable oscillation. The difficulties endured from the XP5Y into the first of the follow-on R3Ys, and the program was terminated due to high costs and the ship's lack of stability in flight."

The Decoupling Matter, I

Among the required capabilities recognized early in this first turboprop installation, noted Holman, was quick disconnection of a crippled engine. "Unless instantaneously removed from the power train by decoupling, the drag of a failed power section would immediately fail the second power section. Of course, reliable decoupling had to be verified on the test stand before any flights, and a realistic failure had to be simulated."

The Engine That Wouldn't

Holman continued: "One power section, number 38, had an internal oil leak and its tailpipe flame grew longer and longer. We just knew that

38 would be a good one to have fail in a natural state so that we could test the decoupler. But it never would give up. It would throw a bright ten-foot flame out over the water of San Diego Bay where the test stand was. When the grunion ran, they liked that light, and everybody filled their lunch buckets and pails with grunion beneath our beacon.

"Since 38 wouldn't fail, somebody came up with the idea of drowning it with water. Well, the housings were magnesium and we really didn't want to put salt water through them. The base fire department came along and said, 'We'll just rig a hose and nozzle up there at the inlet, and that'll get the job done.' That sounded fair enough. Not realizing that the pumper's high pressure nozzle was a straight on/off fitting, we got the engine running to simulate takeoff, and gave the signal. When they opened the valve, the blast of water through the fire section shrank the case and peeled off every blade and vane from stem to stern. Looking down through that thing all you could see was case and barrel. That wasn't too realistic, so we had to think of something else. Eventually, we threw a bunch of junk into one section until the compressor finally went down; the decoupler did its job, and we went on into flight status." But not without a quick reminder that test stands are one thing, airplanes another.

"After my arrival at Convair in San Diego," recalled Mel Beyers, "they had made taxi runs in San Diego Bay and the aircraft was beached for several days. They had scheduled ground runs on all power units and had checked out the aircraft in anticipation of a first flight the next day. Allison service rep Dick Painter and I, as engineering rep, were on hand to make the engine runs. We attempted to start the first power section but the rotor would not turn, nor the second. We checked all eight power sections and only one rotor would turn.

"Concluding that the compressor rotors were locked up, we brought one pair of power sections to the shop, and Bill and I disassembled them and found crystallized salt deposits about 3/8 of an inch deep in the bottom of the compressor case along its full length. We removed the compressor vanes to determine the extent of corrosion in the cases and found only minor pitting—nothing we felt might compromise the safety of the flight. By injecting live steam into the compressor inlet and rocking the turbine rotor we were able to free it. Convair ground crews rigged up a large steam generator and worked on the aircraft while Bill and I reassembled the engines.

"All units were freed up, the engines installed, and the first flight on April 18, 1950, went about 90 minutes with no major difficulties. The test pilot for the flight was Herman 'Fish' Salmon, a big, raw-boned man who looked more like a Kansas farmer than a test pilot. [Salmon went on to a distinguished career at Lockheed Aircraft, where his work on Allison-powered planes included the XFV-1 Pogo Stick, the C-130, and the Electra.] Taxi runs and flights were followed by a fresh water wash of each power section, then extended rotoring to dry them out. The inlets were fitted with snug covers to prevent the flow of salt-laden air through the engines."

The Sewer Pipe

The XP5Y's T40 power sections were mounted behind the rear wing spar, and the gearbox was mounted forward of the front spar. The power takeoff shafts into the gearbox were about 11 feet long, with intermediate bearings near both gearbox and power section. Although the rig ran smoothly on the ground, when airborne the wings flexed and induced vibrations that cut every early flight short. Night after night the engineers

realigned and repositioned the bearings, which were fixed to the structure to eliminate in-flight vibrations.

Jim Holman takes up the story. "Harry Karcher, chief installation engineer from home office, came out to San Diego, and after looking at the ship and listening to our descriptions, at dinner he drew a sketch with his infamous marker pencil on the restaurant tablecloth. We bought the tablecloth and went along the line of his drawings, isolating the shaft within a 120-inch steel tubular housing not fixed to the wing structure, and this much improved the situation. Of course the shaft housing was called 'Karcher's Sewer Pipe.' It did the job well enough to get on with flight testing."

The Toothless Shark

Jim Holman was also on the team that handled the T40's next installation, in the Douglas A2D Skyshark. The fast, maneuverable fighter-bomber was powered by a single, short extension shaft version of the T40-A-6. The gearbox attached through a rigid structure to twin power sections driving two 14-foot, counter-rotating Aeroproducts propellers. The airplane was so "unbelievably hot that you had to tie it down on the ramp to get full power, or you'd just drag the wheels."

The Skyshark generated another of the Allison legends, recalled vividly by many staffers. Holman's version captures the grit of testing at the frontiers of aviation knowledge:

"The second aircraft had advanced to dive and pullout tests, highly instrumented, and on the next test morning, we watched the takeoff and then stood by the radio listening to communications between Douglas pilot Doc Livingston, the chase plane, and flight control. Livingston made his dive and pullout with his eyes glued on the instruments. He got somewhat level flight and not too much altitude when the chase pilot called and said, 'Hey, Doc, you'd better get out of that thing.' Doc said, 'Why?' 'Well, you've lost the whole front end of it.' Doc said, 'Well, I've still got RPMs and power on my engines.' And then he looked up and said, 'Gee, there's no choppers.' Chase warned him again he'd better get out pretty soon, and Doc replied, 'I can't get out because the canopy's jammed, but I can maintain 160 knots on this thing.' So flight control cleared him to land it. We jumped in our chase car and followed him as he neatly brought it down and came to a stop. We pulled up alongside and got the canopy off. He climbed out, walked to the front of the airplane, and looked down the hole into the inlet. Seeing the garbage that had gone through there, he turned about as pale as the white short-sleeved shirt he was wearing.

"Meanwhile, the front end of the gearbox and the six blades had come to the ground intact, witnessed by a man pretty startled to see this gigantic whirligig coming straight down toward him. We went out and picked it all up. So that kind of wrapped up the A2D."

Premature Pogos

Most T40 test pilots fared less dramatically than Livingston, among them Fish Salmon and J.F. "Skeets" Coleman who flew the era's two most unconventional aircraft. Both the Air Force and the Navy were interested in the tactical utility of VTOL planes, and in 1951 the Navy contracted with Convair and Lockheed for the development of competitive prototypes. Allison's T40-A-6 engine with its dual-prop configuration and 7,100-shp output was the obvious powerplant because counter-rotation was essential so the planes would not spin axially in the hover mode.

At Burbank, Lockheed built one prototype XFV-1 VTOL Pogo Stick (a second airframe was never completed) which made 32 flights from June 1954 until program cancellation in June 1955. Horizontal flight was assessed by fitting the aircraft with a temporary, dolly-like landing gear assembly, and some hovering tests were made with the ship tethered inside the Navy's huge airship hangar at Moffett Field, near Sunnyvale, in northern California. Convair's XFY-1 Pogo made more

Facing page, top: The operational follow-on to Convair's XP5Y was the 80-ton R3Y-1 Tradewind which made many successful transpacific flights. Eleven-foot shafting connected the engine's power section and gearbox. In February 1955 a Tradewind set a U.S. transcontinental flight record of six hours, averaging 403 mph.

Facing page, bottom: One Convair R3Y was configured with pod-slung fuel tanks and reel hoses to assess suitability as an aerial refuelling platform. Four Navy Grumman F9F-8 Panther jets tested the system during 1957 exercises off the Southern California coast.

By 1954 Convair engineering test pilot Skeets Coleman was the dean of VTOL pilots with more than 350 vertical flights in Convair's XFY-1 "Pogo Stick" in San Diego. Tough to fly and difficult to service, the XFY-1 and Lockheed's competing XFV-1 airplane both used Allison's T40 and counter-rotating propellers.

than 350 vertical flights—most in San Diego, some also at Moffett—many piloted by Coleman, and at least one successful transition from vertical to horizontal flight. The airplanes provided much useful data but were ahead of their time, clumsy and awkward. Said one Convair pilot, quoted by aero historian Richard Hallion, "It's awful hard to fly an airplane looking over your shoulder."

The Flight Test Center

Like a wind tunnel for an aerodynamicist, the engine test stand is an essential tool for the engine builder. For both, however, flight provides the only adequate test environment. As new aircraft mature, comprehensive flight testing builds the data base upon which safe and efficient service operation depends.

Airframe builders treat powerplant installation and operation as a major element of an airplane's success. Although they do not intentionally slight engine issues, they understandably hold total aircraft performance as their top priority in a flight test program. "Sometimes," recalls Jim Knott, "it was extremely difficult to work with the airplane people to conduct engine testing because they were unwilling to break into their own schedule. Yet we had to do it to protect our engines. We did a great deal of that and Allison had a good reputation for helping create good power plant installations with all of our customers."

As aircraft development had accelerated in World War II and new V1710 installations had grown more frequent and complex, Allison chief engineer Ron Hazen and his staff became convinced that they really needed a dedicated flight test facility at Indianapolis. "Surely the most significant event in

Allison's early history was successful completion of the V1710," observes Knott, "but the next step and one most important to our development was the creation of a flight test section. Pratt & Whitney and Wright Aeronautical, established engine people, had their own and we had none.

"So in the fall of 1941, a flight test section was created under Harry Karcher, who headed the Installation Engineering Department. We set up the unit at Indianapolis' Weir Cook Airport in the CAA hangar for a short time, and later moved to Roscoe Turner Hangar just east of the present terminal. The section initially included mechanic Ray Freese, test pilot Pinky Grimes, Horace Roberts, who came to us in 1942, and me." Later, test pilots Jimmy Younghans and Bob Hoover joined the staff, followed by Charlie Barnett and Vernon Ford (who won the Bendix Trophy Race shortly before coming to Allison).

In July 1944 the government approved construction and modification of new flight test facilities at a cost of about $700,000, to include hangar, shop, and offices. The building, known as Plant 10, was constructed on land leased from the City of Indianapolis.

Plant 10, A Most Productive Place

The close-knit flight test group grew to about 300, all reporting to Don Berlin, who had considerable autonomy and a separate budget. Unlike today's administration-burdened environment, an engineer might go to the mechanic, draw a sketch of a modification, and, while the work order was going to the boss, the job would be nearly done. Or the instrument man was told about a new idea and he was off and working so that by the next flight he had the instrument ready.

The Diverse Fleet and *Anudderone*

At one time or another during the early 1950s, one of just about every USAF fighter of that era was present on the flight line, including the F-80, F-84, F-86, F-89, F-94, and the XA2D. Among the flying test beds was a bailed Boeing B-17G Flying Fortress with its nose adapted for installation of the test turboprop engine—soon named by an anonymous wag, *Anudderone*.

The first test engine was the T38, derived from a single T40 power section and on its way to emergence as the T56/501. Flight performance evaluation of big turboprops with the B-17 began in April 1949. The marriage of the 15-foot-diameter Aeroproducts propeller to the T38 power section producing over 3,400 hp posed serious compatibility problems that could not be simulated on a test stand, so the basic data had to be derived in the air. The flight test engineering group developed a measurement method that allowed precise evaluation of engine output, particularly during the critical

Typical of the many military aircraft whose engines were flight tested from Plant 10 is the two-man Lockheed F-94 all-weather jet fighter of 1953. Adapted from the P-80/T-33 airframe, the longer F-94 was powered by an afterburning Allison J33-A-33 turbojet.

On its April 1953 maiden flight from Lambert Field at St. Louis, Missouri, McDonnell's unique XF-88B test bed gracefully conceals three engines—two Westinghouse J34 turbojets and an Allison T38 turboprop. The airplane, designed for research on supersonic propellers, was a joint project of the Air Force, Navy, the National Advisory Committee for Aeronautics (NACA), and the Propeller Laboratory at the Wright Aeronautical Development Center.

approach, touchdown, and reverse thrust phases that generate forces on the order of 8,000 to 10,000 pounds.

"Shut It Down!"

In February 1949, following nine years of Air Force service that included production testing of P-39s in Africa, 59 Spitfire missions from England, and 15 months as a prisoner of war (including a daring escape), pilot Bob Hoover joined the flight test staff. Says Hoover: "After the war I went to test pilot school at Wright Field through 1947 and was assigned to the X-1 program at Edwards. Bailing out of an F-84, I was injured when the ejection seat failed and I struck the tail. After recuperating, I was considering a tour at March Air Force Base with P-80s, when I got a letter from Allison. I met Mr. Newill at the Arrowhead Springs Hotel in the San Bernardino Mountains and he offered me a test flying position with Allison."

Hoover left Allison in 1950 to join North American. After a notable career in test flight, Hoover's exhibition flying still earns praise at air shows all across the United States.

One of Hoover's first Allison assignments was with the Boeing and the T38. "I was flying the B-17 one day early in the program," he recalls. "The test-engine operating console was just behind the copilot. We planned to start the T38 at 5,000 ft. Flying along, I said, 'OK, we've got your altitude and airspeed. Crank it up.' He did, and we began to slow down. I added power to the four reciprocating engines. 'Need more power,' I said to the operator. And we started going downhill because I couldn't hold altitude. I said, 'Give me full power or shut it off, we're losing altitude.' He kept fiddling, and we're going down all the while,

and I'm four engines wide open. We got to 1,500 feet and I'm screaming at him, 'Shut it down, we're going to fly right into the ground!' He finally got it shut down, and when we landed we discovered that the prop on the Allison was in reverse. The T38 had been putting out as much power as the other four engines."

Prelude to Disaster

In the transition to jets, production and test facilities first constructed around requirements of the V1710 had been adapted to the new-type engines.

Recalls Bob Lowry: "When I came to Allison in April 1951 as an experimental test engineer, I was assigned to the engine test stands located in Plant 3. These test cells were adapted from the old V1710 stands with big basements and ample room to swing propellers, not originally designed for jet engine testing. There were eight of these test cells and all of the axial-flow turbojet engine development work was done on them. The J33 engine work was done in test cell 8 located at Plant 2 at that time. We were running the model test on the J35-A33 afterburner engine for Northrop's F-89 Scorpion, and early J71 testing was underway. When I arrived at 7:00 a.m. on July 12, 1951, to go to work on the stands, I found the parking lot filled with fire engines and

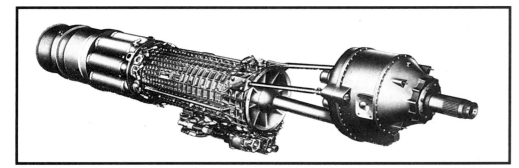

Showing both its T40 parentage and the configuration of its offspring T56, the 2,925-hp T38 turboprop engine of c. 1948 provided vital operating information during evaluation in Allison's B-17 flying testbed and in the Convair Turbo-Liner. During its relatively short service, power output was steadily increased.

The Allison T38 turboprop engine made its first flight in May 1949 as the nose-mounted fifth engine on a converted Boeing B-17G bomber. Operating out of Plant 10, the ship was also flown with the first T56. Flight crews on at least one occasion satisfied their curiosity about whether the big Boeing could fly on the Allison turboprop alone, with all four piston engines shut down. She could.

ALLISONEWS
July 13, 1951, Indianapolis

The calamitous explosion that ripped through the plant 3 test cells early yesterday morning marked the first major catastrophe in the history of the Allison Division. First concern was for eight men believed to be working in the area and therefore possibly trapped in the debris of steel and concrete. Seconds after the explosion, Allison firemen and emergency crews went into action. First to reach the scene from the outside were the fire and emergency departments of Speedway and Indianapolis. Indianapolis and Indiana State Police, Air Force officials and Military Police all worked together to control the fire, to rope off the danger areas and to assist wherever possible in rescue operations.

Here is what happened: at 3:40 a.m. Sgt. Charles Guire, on duty at the patrol switchboard, received a call from an employee in Test Cell 89 reporting a bad fuel leak and requesting that an Allison fire patrolman be sent to the cell immediately. Sgt. Guire promptly dispatched fireman Harry Welborn, who was stationed in the vicinity of Cell 89. Approximately two minutes later, Welborn called patrol headquarters from Test Cell 89. He reported fuel leaking onto the floor of the cell and running into the basement. He said that he needed help promptly to handle the situation and added that if a spark should hit the fuel, it would set off an explosion.

Sgt. Guire immediately called Sgt. Dwight Hastings and fire inspector James Gallagher to request that they proceed immediately to the scene. Before he could finish talking to Gallagher, the explosion occurred. From that minute on, Sgt. Guire was kept busy following the "Allison Emergency Procedure." He made calls to the Indianapolis Fire Dept., Allison Fire Chief Jerry Barnes, other patrol officers, and emergency reserve

patrolmen and firemen. Fireman Welborn and six men from experimental test, working in the stands, were crushed by debris following the explosion.

Rescue crews inched their way through tons of steel and concrete to reach the victims. Torches were applied to steel obstructions; a giant crane was brought in to lift heavy debris and knock down walls which impeded rescue work. All day the crews worked. Six of the victims had been brought out by 10:30 a.m. By late afternoon the seventh body was found.

The explosion demolished the West 20 test cells at plant 3, severing fuel lines to the cells that supported two terrific fires until emergency valves were closed. Impact of the explosion went out through the roof and doors leaving the walls of the cells almost entirely intact.

The explosion lifted both the floor and the roof which then dropped into the tunnel. Of the 20 test cells, six had been converted for testing jet engines, one was partially converted, and one being used for storage. The remainder were not in use. Engines were on four stands, and it is believed the engine on stand 95 was running at the time of the explosion. On the day shift approximately 40 people worked in these cells.

Above: With much of its stupendous force directed upward from below, the blast lifted up the floors above, which then collapsed into the basement to leave such devastation as seen in the test cell corridor, viewed from the south end.

Left: Stark testimony to the ferocity of the energy unleashed in Plant 3 by exploding jet fuel vapors the day before, was the demolished control room for test cells 93-95 photographed on July 13, 1951.

emergency vehicles . . . the eight test cells with their 12-inch-thick walls and floors of concrete smouldering in a heap of rubble."

Approaching The Commercial Market

Among the elements that combined to shape Allison's first substantive entry into commercial aviation in 1950, the most important was probably the company's four years of accumulating experience and growing confidence in turboprop technology. The same performance factors that made the jet-and-propeller combination attractive for some military uses—shorter takeoff, greater payload and range, improved efficiency—clearly had great merit for commercial aircraft. Next, the close and productive association with the technical and management teams at Convair in San Diego and Lockheed in Burbank, both firms with strong multi-engine entries in the military transport and airline market, provided the constant stimulus of shared thoughts.

Precisely how the idea of fitting one of Convair's popular piston-engined 240 airliners with Allison turboprops came about is not recorded, but the results were vital to Allison and American aviation for years to come. Already the British were laying initial claim to important civil market segments with the De Havilland Comet turbojet and the Vickers Viscount turboprop airliners. No American producers had yet shown any public response to that threat.

America's First Turboprop Airliner

In the February 13, 1950, issue of the industry's indispensable journal, *Aviation Week*, an editorial caught some of the import of the Allison-Convair project: "General Motors Corporation's Allison Division comes up with the bold decision to buy a commercial Convair-Liner, install two Allison T38 engines, and test them thoroughly, a significant milestone in our aviation history. It is a happy event to those who were abandoning all hope for a leading role by the free-enterprise system in jet or turboprop development in this country."

Two XT38 2,750-hp engines and a pair of Aeroproducts propellers were installed on the new 240 airframe by Convair in San Diego, and the Turbo-Liner flew for the first time on December 29, 1950. During early flight operations, nearby pilots on the radio hearing a Convair 240 reporting air speeds over 300 mph were incredulous. The airplane in fact, when cleaned up and with both engines operating at their best, could approach 400 mph true air speed, which was stretching the airframe limits a bit.

In spring 1957 the Turbo-Liner was fitted with 501 engines and Aeroproducts 606 turbo-propellers to evaluate the power package for Lockheed's upcoming L-188 Electra airliner. On her first flight with the new package, the Turbo-Liner tucks up her gear following lift-off from Weir Cook Airport, site of Allison's flight test center.

The Hercules Emerges

As the Turbo-Liner began to carry Allison into the commercial transport world from Convair in San Diego, another transport was forming on the Lockheed drafting boards just three hours away in Burbank. In 1951 the Air Force had announced a requirement for a medium-sized logistic and tactical transport, and from a contract for two prototypes would come the four-engined YC-130 Hercules that would ensure Allison's domination of the military transport turboprop marketplace for decades.

The Decoupling Matter, II

In preparing the XP5Y's T40 engines in San Diego in the winter of 1949, the need to prevent drag from a failed engine had been resolved with a decoupling device, but a little bit of Murphy lurked in the decoupler, as Vernon Ford and 10 Allison colleagues discovered over El Paso one suddenly exciting afternoon in June 1952.

Late in 1958 three T56/501-powered transports fly in stair-step formation over central Indiana—top to bottom: the Allison Convair Turbo-Liner; a Convair YC-131C military version of the Convair 340 airliner, and an early Lockheed C-130A Hercules, minus the type's later distinctive bulb-nose radome.

Following flight test work at Edwards AFB, Allison's Turbo-Liner completed an eventful trip to Plant 10, arriving on July 2, 1952.

Having completed one phase of her test program at Edwards Air Force Base, the Turbo-Liner was heading east for a festive public welcome home at Weir Cook after "the longest flight ever made by an American turbine-powered transport." The trip certainly filled that billing. Project engineer Bob Reed, who was also flight engineer for the trip, takes up the narrative:

"We left Edwards at 2:00 p.m. on Sunday, June 17, so we would arrive in Indianapolis on Monday morning, with Vern Ford flying. We weren't in the air long when we developed an engine fire. We landed at Blythe, California, where we changed both engines, and left the following Sunday. We planned a fuel stop at El Paso, and began letting down from 20,000 feet, the throttles at idle. Passing through 12,000, we encountered gusts strong enough to induce momentary negative thrust on the props. And of course both engines promptly decoupled.

"It was a very quiet ride down, and we made our approach hot and downwind. We landed more than a third down the runway, and as soon

as we were solidly on, Vern activated the high-pressure-air emergency braking system. As the main tires locked on the concrete, their tread broke away to damage the flaps, wheel well doors, and some belly skin. We jacked it up and dollied it over to adjacent Biggs Air Base for repairs. The next Sunday, we headed to Oklahoma City and towards home. We arrived on Monday, July 2, about 2:00 p.m.—only two weeks late. With proper adjustment, the decouplers were not a problem again."

Operation Hourglass

By the time the T38 had matured into the 3,250-hp YT56 in 1953, the turboprop's performance was generating increased interest from potential airline and corporate customers. But it would take verified reliability under real operating conditions to convince practical fleet planners that the engine could fly the line day in and day out. And that meant flying time, the more the better.

First came an accelerated Air Force test program in which two YC-131Cs, the military version of the Convair 340, were fitted with YT56 engines and flown for a combined total of 3,000 hours in under eight months. Beginning in May 1955, the 1700th Test Squadron of the Military Air Transport Service flew the two ships out of Kelly Air Force Base, Texas, to and from destinations all across the U.S.

To demonstrate the 501/606 power package, Allison leased a Convair YC-131C from the Air Force in fall 1957 for a 1,000-hour demonstration, "Operation Hourglass." The left-hand engine and gearbox unit was carefully positioned during installation in September. Bright foil protects the air intakes and torque shaft above the two main mounts between gearbox and compressor section.

Continued on page 123

Pete Blanchard's Aeroproducts

The Aeroproducts name, synonymous for an era's innovative propellers and prop controls, holds an honored place in the General Motors and Allison story.

Werner J. "Pete" Blanchard, who had earned his BS in engineering from Kansas State, went to work at Curtiss Aeroplane & Motor Company in Long Island, New York, and in 1929 was made department manager and executive engineer, put in charge of propeller design there. A prolific inventor (between 1932 and 1948, he accumulated more than two dozen propeller and propeller-control patents), Blanchard was particularly interested in both propeller blade design and the notion of controllable pitch to provide the kind of subtle aircraft power management impossible with the fixed-pitch propellers standard from the beginning of powered flight. Increasingly unhappy with the lack of interest in his ideas he found from his immediate

Engineer Werner J. "Pete" Blanchard in 1936 established Engineering Projects, the partnership that would become the Aeroproducts Division of General Motors in 1940. Blanchard's patents include sophisticated propeller blade and hub designs.

superiors at Curtiss, Blanchard determined to set out on his own and resigned late in 1935.

Pete and his wife Juliet selected Dayton, Ohio, as their new home town, partly because of family associations, but mostly because it was the location of Wright Field and the Army Air Corps Materiel Command—the place most likely to be interested in Blanchard's propeller designs. On February 1, 1936, Blanchard and a former colleague from Curtiss, Charles MacNeil, established the partnership of Engineering Projects, and offered the Air Corps their design for a sophisticated hollow steel propeller blade.

The blade designs soon resulted in development contracts, and with additional revenues from the sale of hydraulic propeller hub patents to the Wright Aeronautical Corporation, Blanchard felt sufficiently confident to incorporate his enterprise in 1937. To obtain the capital needed to develop their designs, Blanchard and MacNeil offered one-half their corporate stock to various companies, including Hamilton Standard and Curtiss-Wright. Among the prospective buyers, MacNeil visited General Motors in Detroit, where he spoke with vice president Ernest Breech.

Consistent with the GM corporation's established policy of broad-based involvement with aviation, and recognizing the

At the heart of the 606 is the hub assembly, the propeller's principal structural member. The hub was machined from an alloy steel forging, shot-peened to improve fatigue life, and cadmium-plated against corrosion. A technician at the Vandalia, Ohio, plant in 1958 prepares an Electra unit for shipment.

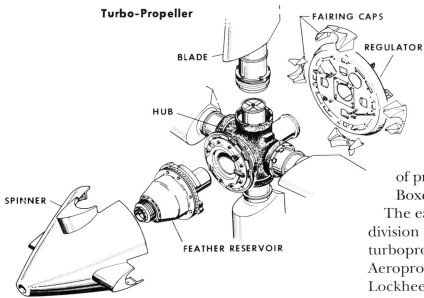

Turbo-Propeller

FAIRING CAPS
BLADE
REGULATOR
HUB
SPINNER
FEATHER RESERVOIR

potential of the Air Corps interest in Blanchard's propeller designs, Breech responded favorably to MacNeil's proposal. At a meeting on April 26, 1939, Breech told Blanchard that GM might wish to establish a propeller division with personnel of Engineering Projects. On June 1, 1940, announced GM board chairman Alfred P. Sloan, the Engineering Projects Company became the Aeroproducts Division of General Motors. Its peak wartime staff of 2,500 employees turned out impressive numbers of propellers for the P-39, P-63, and the P-51 Mustang; and over the Aeroproducts

Vandalia Plant adjacent to the Dayton Airport the coveted Army-Navy "E" banner flew three times.

Charles MacNeil died in 1944, and Pete Blanchard was killed in the crash of his private plane near Columbus, Ohio, in December 1948. With the war's end, employment at the Dayton plant fell to 1,600. Manufacture of propellers for the Fairchild C-119 Flying Boxcar transport sustained the operation.

The early 1950s were optimistic years for the division as Allison began flight testing its turboprop package of the T38 and the Aeroproducts propeller on the B-17G. Early Lockheed C-130s and most Electras, and the Convair 580 each performed superbly with Aeroproducts propellers. In 1952 GM consolidated the division with Allison, and in January 1961 all operations were moved to Indianapolis. The Electra program ended in the early 1960s and, in the growing domination of the commercial and military markets by turbojets, prospects for profitable new propeller production vanished. In order to insure sustained spares and service for the Electra fleet, the decision was made to sell the Aeroproducts assets to Hamilton Standard.

Above: The 13 1/2-ft.-diameter Aeroproducts Model A6441FN-606 Turbo-propeller consists of five elements—its four brazed hollow steel blades, the hub assembly, regulator, feather reservoir, and spinner. The 606 constant speed design incorporates feathering, reverse thrust, selective blade angle for ground operation, phase synchronization, and ice control.

Part of the success of the Convair 580 and Electra sales program was the outstanding performance of the Allison 501 engine and the Aeroproducts 606 propeller in a matched power package. During the 1957 Turbo-Liner test program for the Electra installation, Aeroproducts operations manager R.E. Lynch (left), and Allison general manager Ed Newill visit Plant 10.

Fresh paint gleaming, workmen making haste carefully, engineers checking every detail, Ship No. 886 is prepared for her historic endurance program. In the foreground her No. 2 501-D13 engine is readied.

The tail paint performance was marginal after 1,000 hours, but everything else about "Operation Hourglass" was flawless. The final flight on January 23, 1958, carried top Allison managers. Joining pilot Joseph Thomas (far right) were, from left: crew chief Lloyd Fix, executive engineer Bob Settle, co-pilot John Cyrocki, general manager Ed Newill, assistant general manager Harold Dice, and director of engineering Dimitrius Gerdan.

Next, Allison leased one of the YC-131Cs for an intensive test program of its own, designed to display the airplane's capabilities in a typical commercial schedule. On October 23, 1957, as 300 observers headed by Ed Newill and the engineering staff looked on, "Operation Hourglass" went into full swing when the YC-131C roared down the Weir Cook runway, through a driving rainstorm, for the start of the round-the-clock demonstration of the 501-D13 (the designation chosen for the civil version of the T56) engines and Aeroproducts Turbo-propellers.

Modified at Plant 10, the airplane was flown by six pilot-engineers on the Allison payroll. Often flying out of Phoenix to take advantage of good weather, the ship accumulated 1,057 hours of flying in 88 days, concluding on January 23, 1958. The airframe, basically a cargo version, was fitted with a few passenger seats for demonstration, beds for crew rest, and extensive instrumentation. Included were photo panels of instrument faces with a one-way mirror so engineers could monitor them while a 35mm camera recorded a comprehensive display of readings periodically and on command.

The elusive commercial market proved tough and slow to develop. Recalls Don Davis: "We didn't want to get in the aircraft business, we wanted to sell engines. There was no question that the T56 made a great power plant replacement for the Convair 440s, but we couldn't find any airframer that wanted to take on the program. Airplane makers naturally prefer selling new airplanes to re-engining old ones. We went to Convair and almost pleaded with them to take on the program and they declined, as did Canadair [who had themselves converted three 240s and built 10 new Convairs—the Canadair 540—with Napier Eland turboprops between 1958 and 1961]."

PacAero and the Convair 580

The answer lay on the Pacific Coast in the Santa Monica shops of the PacAero Division of Pacific Airmotive of Burbank, California. An excellent airplane converter, PacAero did the installation and conversion.

The converted airplane was initially called the Allison Super Convair, later the Convair 580—the designation that distinguished the Allison-powered airplane from the competition. Other turbo Convair 240/340 conversion efforts included the 540 with Napier Eland engines and the 600 and 640 with Rolls-Royce Darts, none of which was commercially successful. A concerted effort was mounted to sell the 580 package both to first-time Convair prospects and to operators of the piston-powered 240s and 340s, particularly the U.S. regional carriers and smaller airlines worldwide, under program sales manager Frank Walters from 1962.

The first sale of the Convair 580 was made to General Motors Air Transport Section (GMATS), which ultimately owned eight and used them most successfully carrying GM executives and others worldwide.

"It was certainly my favorite program," recalls Walters. "We went out to assay the market, ordered the parts, sold the individual customers, then the airlines. The conversion package was consistent—engines, propellers, modifications to wings, tail, and brakes to accommodate the additional power, a total package that came to something over a million dollars in related work. Beginning with the Turbo-Liner in 1950, we took it all round the country, and nobody wanted to be first."

Among the company's best sales tools for naturally cautious air carrier operators was the route demonstration. Typical was the July 1966 tour for North Central Airlines that flew a 1,024-mile sample of route segments— Minneapolis to Minot via Grand Fork with intermediate stops, returning to Minneapolis via Bismarck and Aberdeen. The demo aircraft posted a

Above: By 1971, 172 Convair/Allison 580 passenger liner conversions had been sold, primarily to U.S. regional airlines. Many were still in profitable service two decades later, their Allison 501s having achieved some of the airline industry's best ever maintenance records.

Facing page: Pop Kreusser, assistant to general manager Ed Newill, had earned distinction for his work for Julius Rosenwald in creating Chicago's world-renowned Museum of Science and Industry in 1929. Kreusser conceived Powerama (facing, page, top) and guided its development. The elaborately-machined 24-hourglass (whose base appears to be a plated inlet mount assembly of a J33) contained one billion tiny ceramic beads that passed through the center at the rate of 11,500 per second.

28 percent improvement over published schedules (and five percent better than Allison's own prediction).

Change Your Sign

Not every pitch went according to plan, as Jim Knott remembers: "We were trying to sell the 580 to the Air Force, and after quite a bit of doing, we had persuaded Chief of Staff Gen. Curtis LeMay to come for a demonstration flight at Washington National Airport. We'd brought the Hourglass ship, and beneath the logo on the tail we'd painted, '1,000 Hours Without A Failure.'

"LeMay showed up with two or three aides and got in the airplane and sat down. Much to our shock one of the engines would not start. We tried and tried and tried. We'd had a little minor trouble and we thought it was fixed. But today it would not start. So after trying for about 15 minutes we had to call it off. LeMay had said nothing. He got out of the airplane, stopped, looked back at the tail, and said: 'You better change your sign.' And with that he disappeared."

Allison's Own Museum

On February 9-10, 1954, Allison opened the Powerama Museum on the main floor of Plant 3. Handsomely laid out and incorporating state-of-the-art museum design and imaginative lighting, the spacious display included current Allison products, exhibits tracing the company's historical development, and lots of gleaming working models.

Overhead hovered an armada of builders models of 51 aircraft types that Allison engines had powered from 1937. On polished oak stood a U.S. Army Patton M-46 tank that could be driven in place to demonstrate the wonders of the crossdrive transmission. Everywhere were photomurals, models of trucks and buses and locomotives, diagrams, dioramas, real engines and transmissions.

Taking advantage of the opening day gathering of VIPs and the press, Ed Newill made ceremonial presentations to the USAF and the Army Ordnance Corps of Allison's 25,000th jet engine and its 30,000th military transmission.

A constant source of pride to employees, the Powerama was open to the public and attracted as many as 80,000 visitors each year. The aircraft displays were dismantled in 1984 and removed to Plant 8 as the Powerama gave way to needed office space. Recently the Powerama was reorganized for transmission displays and a special exhibit honoring founder Jim Allison.

Jet Engine Production Records

While new projects developed, manufacturing continued to pay the bills. As factory and flight experience built up, Allison's production engines continued to accumulate performance and durability records. On August 23, 1951, at Williams Air Force Base, Arizona, the J33-A-23 became the first J33 to operate 1,000 hours before overhaul. Allison delivered from production the first T40 turboprop engine in April 1952. Three months later two J33 jet trainers set world records for endurance and utilization flying, and 58 Allison J35-powered Republic F-84Gs made the first mass jet flight across the Pacific. By March 1, 1953, Allison J33 and J35 engines had logged 2.5 million flight hours.

Paths Not Taken

Corporate destinies may be said to evolve as much by options not chosen as those pursued. As Allison approached the 1960s, its future was about to be rigorously defined by a curious combination of fate and deliberate choice.

CHAPTER 8
Evolving

General Motors and Allison,
changing corporate and division goals.
Allison and high technology engines.
The jet engine industry,
military and civil markets;
Allison, P&W, GE.
Stratojets and 707s, Rolls-Royce and
the Spey. TF41 development
and trial in Corsair II.
T56/501; Hercules, Electra, Orion.

*Previous page:
Heading out . . . a heavily-
laden A-7 Corsair II labors
for altitude as she leaves
the flight deck of the USS
Constellation (CVA-64) in
the Gulf of Tonkin off the
Vietnam coast in 1968.*

I n a free market economy, businesses must conform to the laws of supply and demand.

Determined to see Allison thrive as a viable company—not merely as a hobby for his employer—Norman Gilman had recognized those laws when he strove to develop the V1710 to fill a demand he correctly anticipated from 1929.

Ten million bearings and 70,000 engines in six wartime years amply verified the company's productive capacity. But during its first three decades—from the freedom of the auto racing shop before World War I through the era of Liberty engine uprating and bearing-making between the wars to the production of World War II—the Allison organization had not directly confronted conventional economic reality. Even the automotive-allied production that sustained Allison plants in the first years after World War II had more the look of "any port in a storm" than straightforward, hard-headed business.

Defining the Division

In fact, Allison was—and would remain until its first reorganization into two divisions in 1983—a unique and sometimes puzzling operating unit of uncertain status within the General Motors family. No matter the good intentions of Detroit, it remained after 1950 or so for the Indianapolis operations to define their own corporate character if their enterprises were to survive.

That Allison's two divisions—each established by the beginning of the 1990s as a leading producer in its worldwide market sectors—approach the 21st century with excellent, if not untroubled, prospects for future prosperity suggests that adequate definition was achieved.

The Bedrock

While Allison sought to make its way within the framework of General Motors and in the world at large, three company characteristics emerged early and continue to dominate the corporate culture.

First is Allison's spirited body of loyal and caring employees whose skills, energy, and devotion have defined the company from the day in 1915 when Jim Allison put Johnny Aitken on the payroll. Second is a set of values that holds product and service integrity above near-term gain. Whether a tech rep laboring through the night to balance a balky prop so a dawn flight may depart on time from La Guardia, or entire departments assaulting the unknown cause of an engine failure, Allison's determination to stand by its customers is legendary. And finally is the discipline of engineering—its inherent curiosity, its delight in search and discovery, in solving tough problems, in making things work. Allison's strength has long derived from its imaginative engineers.

The Garage and the Hangar

In the 1950s the newly-made transmission team began to secure Allison's place on and off the nation's highways, battlefields, and proving grounds with torque converters, powershift, automatic, and crossdrive transmissions.

The company's aviation-oriented managers and engineers faced two related and simultaneous barriers. The first lay in the new and increasingly competitive arena of jet engine development for both civil and military markets. The second was within the top management in Indianapolis and Detroit.

A Different Kind of Competition

The competition from General Electric and Pratt & Whitney for military engine development contracts and entry into the pending commercial jet transport market was both exceedingly tough and inherently different from the sort of competition to which GM's automotive-trained executives were accustomed.

In place of rigorously cost-controlled, efficient annual production of hundreds of thousands of units, minor model changes, and the flexibility of consumer marketing, came high-stakes, winner-take-all confrontations. These contests called for up-front commitments of great quantities of research and development dollars, engineering talent, and exhaustive testing. All these "bet your company" tactics offered no assurance that the best effort would win *any* market share in a given product class—or even anything more than reimbursement for a fraction of prototype costs.

The attitudes of auto and aero men whose careers had developed primarily in one or the other discipline often contrasted sharply. Such conflict occasionally culminated in faulty policy or operational decisions. But in 1950 so much was new to everyone that learning and discovery dominated every manager's schedule.

Balancing Competing Viewpoints

Overseeing Allison's pathfinding until his retirement in 1960, division general manager Ed Newill was capable of boldness when he was persuaded of the need. However, his people-oriented management style favored a balanced, conservative approach to major issues. An engineer by training and a GM man through-and-through, Newill had learned aircraft on the job with Allison from his arrival in 1943. His attitude toward the company's aviation work, then almost exclusively under military contract, was that of a loyal, patriotic man who would endeavor to meet whatever reasonable demands might be made by the customer in the national interest.

Jim Knott, then manager of the Dayton office, had come to Allison in 1940 as an installation engineer. His first job out of the University of Michigan Engineering School had been as a flight engineer on Pan American Airways' Boeing 314 Clippers.

Named chief of customer engineering service in 1945 and manager of sales engineering in 1949, Knott spent most of his Allison apprenticeship dealing daily with the Army Air Corps and Navy powerplant procurement people and with airframe builders. One result was Knott's strong belief in product development leadership: "We wanted to put our profit money into R&D so we could start to develop an engine and try and sell it. Because I was out on the road with the aircraft people, I knew what the other engine people were doing, almost like a spy.

"Ed Newill, and other senior people with GM backgrounds, said, in effect, 'if you can sell something and get government funding for it, then we'll do it.' But the competition would develop a core engine, a performance demonstrator, and then say to the customer, 'Now we can adapt this to your likely applications.'

"Take the P&W twin-spool J57/JT3 for example, that got them into both the 707 and the DC-8. Our single-spool J71 didn't have the fuel consumption, and Charlie McDowall and Dim Gerdan bootlegged a J35 compressor and a T38 compressor on a test stand side by side to simulate a two-spool engine that showed much improved fuel consumption. I went to Ed Newill and said, 'This is what we've done, and unless we pursue it, P&W will run away with the market.' But chief engineer Ron Hazen was not persuaded, and Newill deferred to his judgement.

"By the 1960s the competition was on among GE, P&W, and Allison for any kind of installation. We were presumed [by the military] to belong to fighters, not to long range airplanes, and our failure to initiate the more advanced design engine prevented us from being seriously considered in those early days. Later we achieved designs that were completely competitive, but at that time momentum favored P&W and GE who were firmly established in bombers and transports. Allison had to play 'catch up'."

Vital Support on Occasion

"Detroit sometimes just didn't seem to understand what we were doing," continues Knott, "and yet they could be very receptive and responsive. Take for example the 1955 Plant 8 engine test facility, a $75 million project. Locally we'd convinced management that we had to do it. GM president Harlow Curtice and the executive committee came down to Indianapolis. In making the slide presentation, I described what the Air Force was planning, the coming of supersonics, the need for our proposed facility. Suddenly Curtice turned around in his front row chair and said, 'Fellows, this sounds like a helluva deal to me, let's do it.' The lights came on. Curtice was intrigued and convinced. Without that plant there would be no Allison today. From then on, we started to become a high tech outfit, conscious of high technology."

The Long Range Turbojet Hurdle

Even with the best corporate support, crossing the threshold into new market territory was sometimes a matter of fortune not technical excellence. The multi-engine, long-range turbojet market is a case in point, and one that long frustrated Allison efforts.

In Jim Knott's words: "A good example was the Boeing B-47, the first medium-range jet bomber—and proposed by Boeing with our J35 engines. GE's competing J47 was a little heavier and not quite so fuel-efficient, but there seemed to be a feeling at the Air Force that GE should be given a better position in production. And although Boeing formally protested that the airplane would not perform as well with the J47 as the J35, Gen. Bill Irvine still selected the J47. Out the window went one of our best chances to enter the bomber field."

The Perfect Match, Nearly

In 1958 engineering director Dim Gerdan and assistant director Jim Knott went to Derby, England, to discuss with Rolls-Royce a cooperative development to capitalize on the basic Rolls bypass engine designs. A partnership with Allison would give Rolls both a U.S. marketing and production base and an engineering staff to adapt engine designs for American installations and certification.

Beginning in 1959 the program quickly evolved an attractive family of Allison/Rolls-Royce (AR) bypass engines. The star was the AR963-6, rated at 12,170 pounds thrust for take-off, adapted from the RB.163 Spey (originally designed for the Hawker Siddeley Trident airliner which preceded the 727 by two years). The AR963-6 incorporated Allison modifications for the Boeing Model 727 tri-jet airliner. The 727 concept had already been sold to both Eastern and United airlines without the final engine selection being made.

The engine competition for the 727 matched the AR963 with P&W's JT8 engine. Boeing's original performance calculations were based on the AR963, but engine choice was left to the airlines. United's chief engineer,

115196

Bill Mensser, found either engine acceptable, but Eastern chose the JT8. The decision was reportedly made by board chairman Eddie Rickenbacker, despite a personal visit from GM vice president Ormand Hunt.

Recalls Knott, "Rickenbacker chose the JT8 not for technical reasons, but because he knew the P&W management team personally and had only recently become acquainted with Allison and Rolls people."

But for that decision, Allison might have been the leader in airline turbofan engines for generations with installation in the 727. More than 1,700 727s were sold worldwide.

The Spey discussions with the British also included possible sales to the U.S. military, and a bit of engineering work was done and ways of handling the drafting worked out, but none appealed then to Uncle Sam.

Breakthrough: the Spey Becomes the TF41

Reminiscent of Allison's experience in two world wars and the Korean conflict, another wartime scenario was about to pull those preliminary collaborative drawings off the shelf to meet several urgent needs.

In the mid-1960s—as the Vietnam War continued unabated and the demand for both military and civil transport jet engines strained U.S. production capability—a memo from defense secretary Robert McNamara urged the armed services to secure an engine source to supplement GE and P&W. At the same time, the Air Force was planning to update Ling-Temco-Vought's versatile A-7 Corsair II fighter-bomber, then operational with P&W's TF30 turbofan. The pieces were in place. The moves came swiftly.

With a smile and some expansive gestures, engineering director Mike Hudson compresses the company's second quasi-legendary jet engine start-up story.:

"The Air Force colonel told to implement McNamara's memo called our Washington office. He said, 'Will you folks Americanize this Rolls-Royce engine for the A-7?'" After a major proposal and a tough sales job with Vought and the government, agreement in principle was established among the governments, Rolls, LTV, and Allison. The complex task of refining the Spey core into the 14,250 lb.-thrust production engine called the TF41 got underway with suitable bureaucratic complications.

Thrust Equals Paper Weight

The TF41 contract process was a special challenge, remembers Don Davis: "When we set out to negotiate with Rolls-Royce, they pretty much looked on the process as 'granting another license to the colonies.' The U.S. government, on the other hand, wanted officially to contract with Allison and 'one of Allison's subcontractors would be Rolls-Royce,' with all the standard federal subcontract regulations rigorously applied. Rolls-Royce had never been treated that way by their own government, let alone by colonials. The British defense contract requirements at the time, I learned, all fit in a small manual, largely written by Rolls-Royce. We spent much of a year getting the arrangement for Rolls lined up and approved by our government."

Allison, as prime contractor, was manufacturer and tester of the production engines, while the firms jointly designed and developed the engine through qualification testing. Rolls provided about half the final parts, Allison the balance.

"We laughed at the absurdity of the contract's standard contingency provision about bankruptcy for either General Motors or Rolls-Royce," recalls Davis. "With the RB.211 problems and all, Rolls did go bankrupt, of course, but the legality did not interfere with the project. Rolls continued to provide their components and we managed to stay mostly on schedule. At peak we shipped about 25 engines each month."

The AR Team

The two companies wasted no time in building a close-knit project group of great capability. Bill Thomas picked five design engineers to accompany him as a team to Rolls-Royce in the summer of 1966. They were integrated within the Rolls-Royce organization, rapidly learned the Spey, and got on with the TF41 so quickly that an engine was running on the test stand in about 14 months.

For the first year or so, there were some 30 engineers in Derby, and Rolls sent six or eight engineers and production coordinators to Indianapolis. The schedule was tight and the first production engine was ready in 30 months. Those schedules rank among the shortest of their kind

ever. In October 1967, two weeks ahead of schedule, the first prototype ran successfully in Derby. Only five months later the U.S. prototype ran in Maywood. The TF41-powered LTV A-7D made its highly satisfactory maiden flight at Edwards Air Force Base in September 1968.

Key to attaining TF41 schedules was Herbert Karsch, a no-nonsense manager and tireless organizer, who also had directed early GM missile and rocket research. He not only coordinated the TF41's accelerated development but later directed much of the work that solved the engine's operationally-revealed problems.

Deadly, Elusive Gremlins

In 1969-1970 came a series of A-7 accidents traced to catastrophic failure of the TF41 turbine section. Suddenly an engine that had shown exemplary reliability during two years of Vietnam combat was failing between 200 and 400 hours on training and non-combat missions. The search for solutions led Allison's TF41 team into an accident investigation exercise that would yield not only a fix for the immediate problems but several other enduring benefits as well.

Because the episode offers a vivid example of Allison and its classic engineering at work, a review of the TF41's problems help's chronicle the company's heritage. The following synopsis is adapted freely from the recollections of senior engineering managers.

While the TF41 had performed well in missions whose pattern usually included straight takeoff, direct ordnance delivery, and conventional landing, it was determined that training and formation flights with protracted variation of throttle settings led to failures. Although it took little work to track the failures to the turbine, a great deal more testing was needed to isolate the uncontained cracking of a spacer ring between turbine disks. Even more sophisticated and determined detection was applied to isolate the origin of the cracking in low-cycle, intermittent, high frequency vibration.

The Gyroscopic Test Stand

Suspecting that the problem might emerge in high-stress maneuvers, Allison designed and built a gyroscopic test stand in which an engine

The Allison/Rolls TF41 performed superbly in Vietnam combat assignments, driving LTV A-7 aircraft at speeds up to 650 mph. Following a series of accidents on training flights in 1969, exhaustive testing led to redesign of a turbine component and restoration of the engine to its extraordinarily high level of reliability. Gas flow is left to right.

could be rotated around all its axes while under full power. When it was decided to build the rig, the engineers said they could have drawings in 30 days. That Thursday afternoon, Karsch said to them: "Well, we're breaking ground on Monday morning and it would be better if we had drawings." In 30 days the test stand was built and the first engine tested. The gigantic $500,000 apparatus, with pipes and tubing and tons of concrete, was later dismantled, moved, and rebuilt at the Navy Aero Propulsion Center (NAPC) in Lakehurst, NJ. But the clue lay not in the attitude of the engine but in its operating cycle.

The spacer ring between two turbine disks was cracking all the way through, triggering disintegration of the turbine, usually on takeoff. The cause of the cracking was subtle and difficult to isolate for observation: fatiguing vibration that occurred only briefly in the flight envelope. When the engine was fired up, the ring heated quickly, the disks slowly; so the ring would start to lift off its pilot and induce a transient vibration, but only for a short time during acceleration of the engine. The fix was direct: remove the spacer and redesign the sleeve.

You'd Better Be Right

When the engineers were confident that they had the answer, an engine was fitted with the new prototype sleeve for flight test in a Navy A-7E at Edwards AFB. The afternoon before the first scheduled

From design to first engine test, this half-million-dollar gyroscopic test rig for the TF41 engine took only 30 days to build in 1970. Operating through its full power range, an engine could be rotated around all its axes while performance factors and loads were measured. The rig was later moved to a Navy test center in New Jersey.

flight, Eloy Stevens (the TF41 program engineer at the time) accepted a two-hour conference phone call. On the line from Dallas was a very resistant Vought president Sol Love and two dozen LTV engineers and others. In essence, Love said they would not support the flight of the reconfigured Navy plane the following day.

Early next morning while chairing the regular TF41 task force meeting, Air Force Brig. Gen. Herb Lyon had his call from Love who again declined to support the test. Conferring with the Navy captain who was second in command, Lyons asked, "What is the status on the flight line at Edwards?" The captain said, "The aircraft is on the ramp, the pilot is ready, they'll go on our instruction." Lyon turned to Karsch and said, "What is your recommendation?" Karsch turned to Stevens and said, "Steve?" Stevens said, "There's no reason I know of not to fly that airplane." Lyon said, "Fly the airplane." Karsch said, "Steve, you'd better be right."

In flight the pilot reported no difficulties, and after additional flying through the critical phases, engine teardown confirmed the adequacy of the new sleeve.

Friendly Persuasion

Typical of Herb Karsch's leadership was the matter of getting the new sleeves into operational airplanes swiftly. On a Tuesday when new forgings were ordered for the redesigned part, the supplier said it would take six months. That was reported to Karsch: six days later a truck with 1,000 forgings rolled up to the receiving dock at Plant 5. That night they were being machined. The very last ring to be retrofitted was cracked half-way through, but the Allison team managed to get them all out before another one failed.

The TF41 Program Assessed

Reflecting on some of the broad-scope results of the TF41 program, Mike Hudson expressed deep satisfaction as well as regrets. The regrets, he observed, were that Allison was perceived by some as having problems that they couldn't handle. In fact, the company really cured problems much better than others. Nonetheless, the TF41 didn't secure Allison a foothold in the fighter engine business, simply because there was no follow-on engine program.

However, from the investigation came several extraordinary collateral benefits, believes Hudson. First, the company introduced original and enormously effective engine condition monitoring systems using electronic recording of real inflight data. It provided a gold mine of information from which was designed the Accelerated Mission Endurance Test (AMETS).

AMETS converts real field data into test control tapes so that engine failure can be duplicated for study on the test stand. The program continued Allison's long leadership in engine testing. Moreover, it taught the Air Force that a firm can control destiny by good testing.

"In the collaboration with Rolls-Royce, we benefitted from the synergism of teams," noted Hudson. "The English were extremely confident of their capabilities. They're consummate negotiators. It was a good experience, dealing with the British. In short, the TF41 produced capability at Allison exceeding anything the military customer recognized."

Thanks Anyway

Jim Knott recalls one Rolls program Allison did not choose to join—the RB.211 engine for Lockheed's L-1011 TriStar that was launched in 1968. "We backed out of an RB.211 joint venture. Rolls was determined to win with a three-spool engine, and we didn't think they had the economics down. They bid $675,000 per engine and we thought the minimum might be something closer to $775,000. I went to see Dan Haughton and Karl Kotchian at Lockheed to tell them we wouldn't lose that kind of money. Our decision was a great disappointment to Lockheed."

Allison's caution was well-advised. Financing problems associated with the RB.211 brought the Rolls-Royce aircraft engine business to bankruptcy. Ultimately, both Rolls and Lockheed required financial aid from their respective governments before regaining economic health.

However, as if to prove that life in the aircraft gas turbine business isn't always so perilous, since 1950 the engines spawned by the Allison T40 turboprop rank among aviation's phenomenal success stories. The T56/501 engine family—almost 40 years after inception—shows every sign of flourishing well into the 21st century.

The T56 Dynasty

Derived from the T40 and T38, the T56 design began in 1951, with the first 50-hour test in September 1953. The Convair C-131C first flew with YT56 engines on May 20, 1954. The first production installation came on a Lockheed C-130 Hercules; the maiden flight was made at Burbank, California, on August 23, 1954. Total production from 1954, including some 1,200 industrial units, is now more than 16,000 engines.

"One of the reasons that the T56 was so successful," believes Bob Hicks, "was the amount of testing done on the engine. It's been tested more thoroughly than any engine that I'm aware of over the last 50 years. Before the engine entered production, there had been, I believe, thirteen 150-hour tests run. Two engines had flown on a converted Convair for 1,000 hours each. Those same engines were then examined and some refurbishment done with very minimal parts replacements and then they were run another 1,000 hours on Allison test stands before the Electra program got underway. The engine was first flight tested in the B-17 testbed out of Allison Plant 10, and testing continued in the four-engine YC-130 and then, as the 501, in the Electra."

An Early Record

Allison Flight Test brought an early C-130 production airplane to Indianapolis in September 1956 to test the T56 operating in the airplane. The goal was to evaluate the installation and improve various engine systems.

Much early flying was devoted to evaluating the automatic adjustment of the engine's fuel flow on reaching higher altitudes and colder temperatures. The hydro-mechanical fuel schedule evolved through many locked-throttle climbs to altitude, recording engine data enroute. As part of this operation, an Allison crew set an unofficial world altitude record for C-130s in late 1956. With Dick Petercheff in command, Bob Wendling as co-pilot, Bob Lowry flight engineer, and Bob Reed technical observer, they took the C-130 to 40,400 feet.

Lowry noted that, "When Lockheed Flight Test heard about this, they hardly could stand to have the upstart Allison Flight Test Operation hold the world record. So within a matter of weeks they flew a C-130 to 42,000 feet. They took the record away from us—which was probably as it should be, since they build the airplane."

Exhaustive Allison testing has marked each development phase of the engine, notes Bob Wente: "A T56 testing milestone came with the testing

Allison test pilots Dick Petercheff (left) and Luke Stear delivered a production C-130 from Lockheed's Marietta, Georgia, plant in October 1956, to Plant 10 for continuing engine tests. The C-130's high wing permitted the T56 air inlets to be located on an efficient straight-line path below the gearbox. To minimize foreign object ingestion on low-wing installations, such as the Electra's, the intake was placed above the gearbox.

The Lockheed C-130's efficient wing and great power permitted extraordinary short field performance from unimproved runways, among other advantages, and thousands of the planes serve in air forces worldwide. Propeller-tip vortices reveal a supersaturated atmosphere as this Royal Australian Air Force Hercules climbs away in the early morning. By 1983 more than 1,700 C-130s had been built.

of the complete Grumman E-2/C-2 power package in our test rig. Called 'The Knotter,' it simulated carrier deck landing conditions to test the complete nacelle, engine, and propeller structures. The stand could produce over 20 Gs and one million inch-pounds of bending force. Deck landings equivalent to 21 Gs and 1 million inch-pounds of torque were put into the structure with the engine running."

The T56 Creators

Bob Hicks, test department representative on the project in its infancy, identified leaders of the original T40/T56 design team under engineering director Ron Hazen. Among them were Jack Fetters, chief engineer for power turbine engines, and John Wheatley, chief project engineer. Gordon Holbrook, who joined Allison from the Turbo Engineering Company and would eventually become director of gas turbine research and engineering, earned the nickname, "Mr. Turboprop."

The principal component designers were Joe Barney (compressor), Don Zimmerman (turbine), and Victor Peterson (reduction gear). John Cartwright became famous for his work on the celebrated torquemeter from the mid-1950s until his retirement in 1984,

During the 1960s, Long Island's Grumman Aircraft Engineering Corporation created two T56-powered aircraft for U.S. Navy carrier operations. Grumman manufactured E2A Hawkeye early warning radar planes for long-endurance loiter (bottom), and C2A carrier-on-board-delivery aircraft (top) for carrying high-priority personnel and supplies to and from carriers at sea.

Continuing the company's commitment to imaginative testing, "The Knotter" test rig was built to simulate aircraft carrier conditions for the T56 installation on Grumman's E-2 and C-2 aircraft in the late 1960s.

when his colleagues honored him with a plaque inscribed, "Champion of the torquemeter mid-bearing."

The Look Is Misleading

While an untrained observer can scarcely tell the earliest T56 from the latest version, the engine has grown from 2,800 hp to 5,000 hp (for the industrial version), with countless improvements ranging from metallurgy to geometry.

The current Series IV T56 is largely the result of the determined work of Frank Verkamp and Al Wilson that began in 1976 when Lockheed

California sought to sell the government on the idea of an improved T56 for the P-3 Orion anti-submarine warfare (ASW) aircraft.

With Pete Tramm's and Dick Alverson's re-designed compressor, a "paper T56" offered 10% specific fuel consumption SFC improvement. Follow-on work under the Air Force Engine Model Derivative Program (EMDP) led to specific fuel consumption (SFC) improvements of 12.8 percent and power increases of 24 percent. Intended first to improve the carrier performance of the Grumman E-2 airborne early warning aircraft, the engine was later run in Lockheed's Super C-130 high technology test bed.

Lockheed's Electra, The Pilot's Airliner

The Convair Allison Turbo-Liner of 1950 holds its place in history as the first U.S. turbine-powered airliner. By most criteria, however, America's second turbo-prop commercial transport, and the first designed from inception for turboprop engines, is the more technically and historically significant airplane.

In autumn 1954 at the California division of Lockheed Aircraft Corporation, studies were begun for a small, high-wing transport to meet a tentative American Airlines specification. Initial designs for the CL-303 were projected with twin Rolls-Royce Dart or Napier Eland turboprops. Continuing market studies urged a larger airplane, and with input from Eastern Airlines, Lockheed designers went to the four-engine, low-wing CL-310. By summer 1955, using fresh data from the T56 engines on their new C-130s, the Burbank team chose Allison's commercial T56 derivative, the 3,750-shp 501-D13, to power the substantially upsized L-188.

The blunt-nosed, assertive-looking airliner was named by chairman Robert Gross to recall his Lockheed Aircraft Corporation's first airplane, the Electra 10 of 1933.

American Airlines became the Electra launch customer in June 1955 with an order for 35, followed by Eastern in September with 40. The maiden flight, eight weeks ahead of schedule, was made in December 1957. Federal certification was earned in August 1958.

The 58-ton Electra typically cruised at 370 mph, carried up to 104 passengers, and was intended for medium-range flights. Its range was some 2,360 miles with maximum payload. Passengers were pleased with the plane's quiet cabins that contrasted with the noisy pounding of conventional piston-powered airplanes.

Like the C-130 Hercules and P-3 Orion, from its very first flight the Electra earned pilots' praise for reassuringly nimble throttle response, especially at the lower speeds required for maneuvering during approach

The first T56 turboprop engine was shipped in 1954. Thirty-five years later more than 14,000 had been built, with no end in sight. The 1987 production edition of the T56/501D Series III engine retains the family's basic remote gearbox and torque tube layout. The 5,000-shp, 14-stage, 1,835-lb engine operates at a constant 13,820 rpm. Sixty nations operate aircraft powered with the engine that has accumulated more than 130 million flight hours.

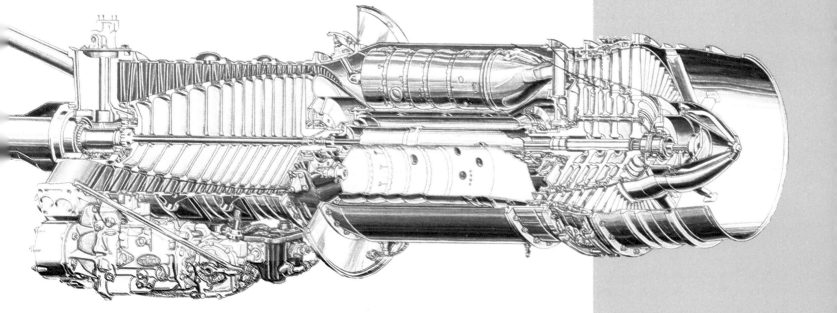

The Aeroproducts turbo-propeller was turned slowly while mated to a 501D engine on the test stand in a 1957 time-exposure that emphasized the low frontal area of the Electra power package. Nacelle design was such that the 3,750-hp engine actually delivered more power installed on the airplane than on the test stand.

and landing. Providing a margin of safety unprecedented in large transports, the Electra's flexibility of control derived from the designed relationship between a powerful engine, a precisely controllable propeller, and a sophisticated wing.

The engine and prop turned at near-constant speed throughout the flight envelope, from full power to full reverse. Virtually immediate increase in available thrust was only a matter of increasing fuel supply. The ship response was as fast as the change in propeller blade angle, with no wait for increased rotational speed. The props washed huge quantities of air over the wings for additional lift generation.

As Bob Lowry remembers more than one airline pilot saying after a first flight, "For once we've got enough power in an airplane."

The Unit Exchange Program

During his employment at GM's Electro-Motive Division in the late 1940s, Allison assistant general manager Harold Dice had observed

Power sections for T56/501 engines in their build-up stands move through final assembly preparatory to mating with their gearboxes, c. 1960.

The first 501-D13 engine with 1,000 hours of service time—the equivalent of some 400,000 miles—was removed at Eastern Airline's Miami maintenance base for overhaul in June 1959. Eastern was the first airline to put the Electra into service. On the carrier's pioneering Washington-New York-Boston Shuttle flights, the airplane was especially effective.

EMD's powerplant exchange program with railroad customers. EMD overhauled locomotive powerplants at its La Grange factory and technicians were able to spot and correct problem patterns while building customer confidence.

At the outset of the Electra program, Dice recommended a similar program in which airlines returned their engines to Allison for repair and

*In order to continue testing
the 501 engines in the
installed environment and
develop the most efficient
operations and maintenance
procedures for the airlines,
Allison bought the first
production Electra
(airframe #006) to operate
out of Plant 10. In 1961
when her test service was
completed, the Allison ship
was sold to the Los Angeles
Dodgers baseball team.*

overhaul and were provided "exchange" replacements. "As the 501s came back for service," noted Bob Hicks, "our engineers and technicians inspected them for early warnings of possible problems, an immense help in refining the engine to be one of the world's most dependable."

Electra Optimism

The early Electra days were happy times for Allison, optimism for the airplane infecting everyone.

Dave Newill particularly recalls the pleasure his grandfather Ed took in joining Lockheed's worldwide sales tour with the demo airplane. "On demonstration flights, while the prospective customer's pilot was at the controls, Lockheed's Fish Salmon would shut down one engine, then another. Then, as the ship cruised along with no perceptible reduction in speed, one of the staff would point out the window to show the VIPs the shut down engines."

A Troubled Career

Lockheed began Electra deliveries in late 1958. Eastern inaugurated service on January 12, 1959, between New York and Miami. American flights began 11 days later between New York-LaGuardia and Chicago-Midway. Other airline orders included National, Braniff, Northwest, Pacific Southwest, Western, Ansett/Australian National, Qantas, Trans-Australia, Cathay Pacific, Garuda, Tasman Empire, and the lone European operator, KLM Royal Dutch.

While airlines praised the operational performance of the powerful and efficient airplane, two decisive factors limited total orders to only 170 Electras before the program terminated in January 1961. The first factor was timing. The Electra was simply overtaken in the marketplace by the turbojets, led by Boeing's 707 that began service in December 1958.

The second factor struck grimly with the midair disintegration of a Braniff Electra over Texas in September 1959 and again on March 17, 1960, with the similar crash of a Northwest Electra near Tell City, Indiana.

Whirl Mode

Besieged by press and politicians to ground the Electra, Federal Aviation Administrator Elwood Quesada instead imposed a speed limit of 295 mph on the planes while Lockheed, Allison, and the Civil Aeronautics Board sought to isolate the accidents' cause and devise a way to prevent recurrence.

The accidents' cause was identified as progressive structural failure in turbulence of an airframe previously damaged as a result, for example, of a heavy landing. If the powerplant structure had suffered slight damage in this way, not significant in itself, it was possible for subsequent turbulence to initiate an oscillation of the engine and propeller which did not damp out. Undamped, the motion led to nacelle vibrations which amplified to "whirl mode," and then to wing flexing and ultimate failure at the wing root. Careless press reports characterized the situation as "the wing came off."

The LEAP

Wayne McIntire remembers his close involvement with the critical Electra situation. "In assessing what might happen if part of the engine mount system failed, our analysis revealed the so-called "whirl mode" phenomenon. We took a T56 carcass to determine how many pounds of force the mounting structure had to absorb and in which direction. In the 'mine shaft,' [test pit] under the tutelage of Lockheed, we tested the mount assembly to failure with hydraulic rams on all the structure to see what broke, to determine what had to be done to adapt the nacelle and

In one of the company's milestone commercial sales, Eastern Airlines' board chairman Eddie Rickenbacker (center) announced his plans to buy 40 Lockheed Electras powered with the Allison power package. With Rickenbacker at New York's Ambassador Hotel in December 1955, GM president Harlow Curtice (left) and Allison general manager Ed Newill (right) met the press to announce the transaction.

mount to the wing. We ultimately added two mounts to the gearbox, one upper, one lower.

"Then we installed the new design on all four engines of a test airplane and the Lockheed crew flew it over the California mountains for several days of increasingly severe flying to find the right conditions of load and mach number on the airplane and turbulence that might induce whirl mode to learn what would happen. [On that Saturday] in the Burbank hangar Lockheed had all four engines from the test flights broken down on a table for us to inspect to see what effect the flying with the new mounts might have had on the gear meshes. All four looked fine."

Soon afterward, Lockheed and Allison devised LEAP—the Lockheed Electra Achievement Program—on which the companies were to spend $25 million modifying the entire Electra fleet.

Under LEAP, a modification package of the two additional gearbox mounts, nacelle stiffeners, and replacement of some wing skin with heavier-gauge panels, was retrofitted to the 145 Electras in service. The modifications were also incorporated into the 25 ships on order. The program was completed by February 1961, when the FAA removed its speed restriction.

The airplane, soon displaced from front line service with major carriers by 707s and DC-8s, found a long secondary career as an economical freighter and with charter operators, particularly in Latin America.

From Electra to Orion

If the Electra's airline career was economically disappointing for Lockheed, its derivative P-3 Orion more than compensated.

Proposed to the Navy in a 1957 maritime patrol and anti-submarine warfare aircraft competition as a development of the L-188 airframe, the P-3 easily won its original research and development contract in 1958.

The modified third Electra airframe was flown as a YP3V-1 aerodynamic prototype in May 1958. By November 1959 it was converted to closely match the eventual production P-3 configuration of 1961 that was powered by T56-A-10Ws rated at 4,500 eshp takeoff power. The 500th airplane was delivered in December 1979, with the eventual total reaching more than 600. Succeeding ships were fitted with constantly improved T56 versions, including the -A-14 rated at 4,910 eshp without water injection.

A New World to Win

Beginning with the T40, the Convair Turbo-Liner, and the big Lockheed airplanes, Allison technology in the constantly maturing T56/501 has dominated the large turboprop business for nearly 50 years.

In contrast to the incremental, almost methodical consolidation of its large turboprop leadership, Allison's meteoric rise to preeminence in the light turboshaft market since 1958 may classify as revolutionary. At a stroke Allison's T63/250 family of engines would bring the turbine's full range of performance advantages to helicopter designers. From battlefield to offshore oil rig, from emergency room to firehouse, Allison small turboshaft engines were about to bring the true utility of aviation to whole new worlds.

Christened "Orion" in ceremonies at Lockheed's Burbank plant in April 1961, the Navy's P3V-1 anti-submarine warfare aircraft exhibits her Electra origins while exercising off the Southern California coast.

CHAPTER 9

Revolutionizing

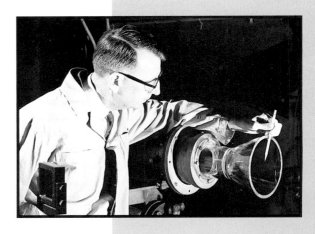

*The Little Engine That Changed
the World of Helicopters.
The Probable Cause;
a Blue Ribbon Campaign.
Product Support and Dealer Networks.
Field Service.
Flightless Birds, Model Contracts,
Turbines for Industry.
The Breech Loader, the Space Age, and
the Frontiers of Science.*

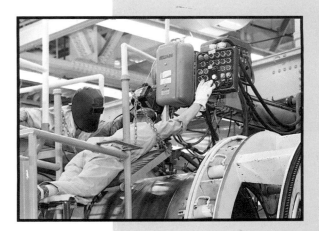

During the late 1950s, U.S. Army planners prepared for a new generation of Light Observation Aircraft (LOA). They left open the question of fixed or rotary wing, but committed early to lightweight turbine power. The engine competition launched in 1957 for a 250-hp gas turbine powerplant was won by Allison in 1958. Development was promptly begun on the T63/250 engine in two configurations: turboshaft for rotary wing and turboprop for fixed-wing aircraft.

The LOA's general mission requirements were those of the old Cessna O-1A (L-19) Bird Dogs—artillery spotting, battlefield command and control, personnel movement, some medical evacuation—the tasks an army commander assigns to light aircraft in a tactical environment. In 1960 the Pentagon settled on the rotary wing and initiated the Light Observation Helicopter (LOH) program. Requests for proposals (RFP) went out to America's helicopter makers. More than 20 concept proposals were submitted by 16 companies. Bell Helicopter, Hughes Helicopters (sold in 1984 to McDonnell Douglas), and Hiller Aircraft were chosen in early 1961 to build three prototype helicopters to be powered by the T63.

At the Edge

Engineering director Mike Hudson ranks the 250 development program among Allison's worthiest achievements. He is not alone in crediting its leadership: "The engine operation was grossly underfunded and understaffed, but here is one of those remarkable, heroic stories of small groups doing whole engines."

When Bill Castle had been named chief project engineer on the new engine and preliminary design was assigned to John Wheatley, the chosen team wasted no time getting underway.

Like their predecessors with the V1710 and the big gas turbines, the 250 group worked at the edges of knowledge. They abandoned the published data to devise major innovations in metallurgy, corrosion resistance, bearings, and castings.

The laws of heat and motion provided little "wiggle room." Tough challenges lay in the small components and in nearly every aspect of materials and design. And vibration headed the list. Because centrifugal force varies as the square of the speed of rotation, doubling an engine's speed multiplies the force four times. A given unbalance at the 250's speeds—up to 51,000 rpm in one recent model—produces 300 times the unbalanced shaking force encountered in the crankshaft of a V1710 with the same unbalance.

Then there was the gas path leakage that compromises performance in turbines of any size. Even with the vastly reduced airflows of the smaller engine, clearances between spinning and stationary parts still had to be maintained. Among the solutions were integrated wheel and blade castings for turbine and compressor wheels that eliminated the need to insert individual blades.

In addition to the core compressor and turbine sections, every component and accessory had to be miniaturized to accommodate the helicopter's crucial weight and space limitations. To devise compact fuel control units with needed accuracy and reliability, for example, the team worked closely with their expert colleagues at Bendix.

One idea that was briefly considered was to eliminate major maintenance and overhaul costs in an expendable engine. With a unit cost of, say, $10,000, when such an engine reached its planned service life of about 500 hours, it would be scrapped.

Hard Won Gains

The initial project goal of an engine of 98 lbs and 250 shp was revised to 109 lbs and a standard-day 317 shp. The reserve was needed to ensure that 250 shp could be delivered on a 95-degree day. Early attempts to run the engine in 1959 showed that many of the new concepts for the lightweight turbine needed reevaluation: it was months before an engine ran as long as five hours. The first successful run was achieved in June 1960.

Development continued during 1960 and 1961 under the original Army contract. In February 1961 the YT63-A-3 engine flew for the first time, in a Bell HUL-1M helicopter. After several attempts, a successful 50-hour Preliminary Flight Rating Test (PFRT) on the -A-3 engine was completed in November 1961, followed by the turboprop YT63-A-1 one month later.

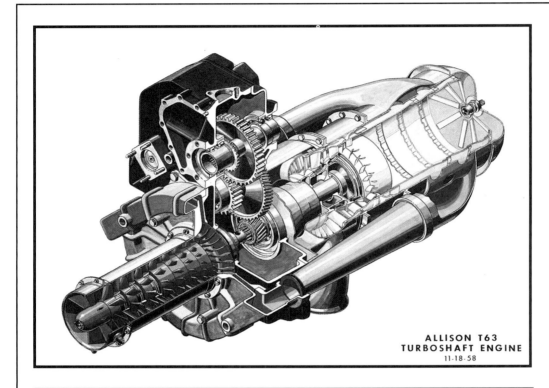

ALLISON T63 TURBOSHAFT ENGINE
11-18-58

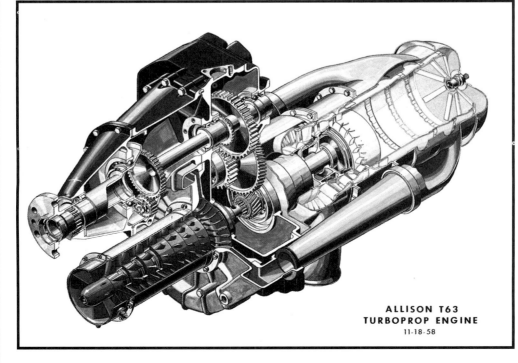

ALLISON T63 TURBOPROP ENGINE
11-18-58

November 1958 cutaway drawings display the early design of the lightweight two-shaft gas turbine T63 engine. The two engine layouts —turboshaft for rotary-wing helicopters and turboprop for fixed-wing airplanes— share a common core.

Inlet air flows from the left through the axial-flow compressor stages, then is forced by the final centrifugal stage through the diffuser into the two lateral air transfer tubes along the outside of the engine to the combustion chamber at the rear. As fuel is injected into the flow, the massively expanded hot gasses pass forward through the turbine's two stages—the gassifier which drives the compressor, and the power turbine which rotates the gear train between compressor and turbine. Spent gasses exit through the exhaust duct below.

In the turboshaft configuration (top) the power to the helicopter's gearbox is transmitted through the gear train to a splined shaft from the topmost gearshaft. In the turboprop layout (bottom), the takeoff shaft transmits its power through the forward planetary reduction gear out to the propeller hub.

As its cutting-edge ancestor, the V1710, had first flown in an obsolete airframe, the YT63-A-3 first flew—in February 1961—in an airframe designed for a reciprocating engine. The Navy's Bell HUL-1M, the first of the new generation of turbine-powered helicopters, was a modification of the piston-driven HUL-1/Bell 47J.

Bolted into their aluminum shipping containers in April 1962 are the first three YT63-A-5 turboshaft engines delivered to Bell, Hiller, and Hughes for their prototype U.S. Army Light Observation Helicopters. Alfred Braun (right) stencils shipping data on the covers while Alfred Teegarden adds silica gel to control moisture in the sealed units enroute.

Good, But How About Upside Down?

Next, the helicopter manufacturers and the Army, presumably after an unpleasant experience or two, decided the engine should be installed with the exhaust outlet directed up. This would eliminate the danger of grass fires from hot exhaust and reduce the infrared signature.

Allison was directed in early 1962 to turn the T63 upside down, in effect, and the first 50-hour PFRT of the inverted engine was completed in March. That variant, the YT63-A-5, became the flight test engine for the three prototype helicopters. In less than four years from contract award, Allison had developed a flight-worthy lightweight turbine powerplant to Army performance standards and adapted it to the specific needs of the aircraft manufacturers.

From Demo to Workhorse

In September 1962, after Jack Wetzler succeeded Castle as chief project engineer, the official 150-hour Model Qualification Test (MQT) on the T63-A-5 engine was completed.

Bell, Hiller, and Hughes continued their flight test development through 1963. Evaluations of five prototype ships were made at Army Aviation headquarters at Fort Rucker, Alabama, and other bases. Separate Allison support crews supported each of the helicopter manufacturers at Fort Rucker.

After technical evaluation and fly-off, Hiller and Hughes were chosen for the final cost competition. Hughes was named winner in early 1965 and began production of the first batch of 1,413 Army helicopters. Deliveries began before the year was out.

A second Army competition for procurement of 2,200 additional LOH helicopters was won by Bell in 1968 with a military version of the JetRanger, the OH-58A. The Navy also selected the Bell design, ordering 40 Allison-powered TH57A Sea Rangers for the training program at Pensacola, Florida.

As U.S. involvement in the Vietnam War deepened, the Army's battle tactics in the daunting jungle environment relied increasingly upon the helicopter's unmatched mobility. The Hughes OH-6As were praised by pilots and support crews as extraordinarily durable, crash-worthy, and reliable.

How Did They Manage Before?

Inevitably, Bell and Hiller determined to enter the commercial market with their helicopters. They hoped to be in the marketplace before Hughes could offer a commercial variant of its successful Army ship.

Bell significantly redesigned their original LOH and introduced the four-place JetRanger, while Hiller adapted their OH-5A into a civil model. Both reached production in 1967. Hughes, meanwhile, had prepared a marketing plan for the Model 500.

At Plant 10 in February 1963, Allison test pilot Jack Schweibold briefs Army Aviation Board president Col. A.J. Rankin on the T63 engine. The exposed power package in the Bell UH-13R test bed reveals engine installation basics. At upper right, the screen mesh canister protects the T63 air inlet, below which the power takeoff shaft connects the engine to the helicopter gearbox at the base of the rotor mast.

Above: During evaluation at Army Aviation headquarters at Fort Rucker, Alabama, the three competing LOH prototypes hover in echelon in 1963. Left to right are the Bell OH-4, the Hiller OH-5, and the Hughes OH-6.

Right: The winning Hughes Army LOH airframe made extensive use of state-of-the-art materials, design, and fabrication. Its extraordinary strength and light weight combined with superior speed and maneuverability to achieve overall excellent performance for its military mission and to affirm the basis for successful commercial adaptation.

Suddenly the small helicopter—from its earliest days an exotic rarity with limited performance, costly to operate, and restricted to military and other subsidized applications—emerged with performance, reliability, and economy to take its place in the civilian marketplace. In the next few years, the uses to which the versatile machines would be put boggled the imagination. And seven out of 10 of them would be powered by one version or another of the reliable 250.

Confirming the new small helicopters' performance advances, in April 1966 a T63-powered Hughes helicopter broke 23 world records for speed, altitude, and distance.

The turboshaft helicopters' higher payload capacity, multi-fuel flexibility, lower vibration, and easy cold-starting all assured swift acceptance by helicopter operators. Allison designers had to work as hard as the manufacturing staff to meet the increasing power demands of growth variants of the aircraft.

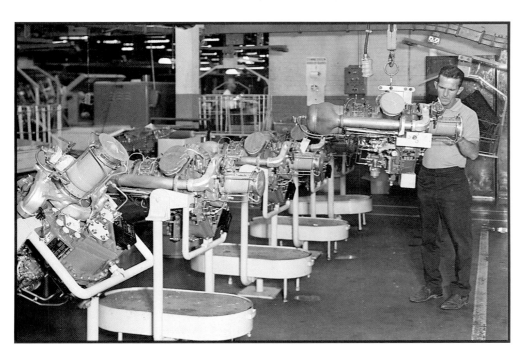

A 400-shp version, the 250-C20, was certified in 1970, followed by the 420-shp -C20B in 1974. The -C20B became the world standard in its class, powering models built by light helicopter manufacturers in the U.S. and Europe, including Italy's Agusta, Germany's Messerschmitt, Boelkow, Blohm (MBB), and Aerospatiale of France.

Maturing an Engine

During the 250's introductory period, two programs contributed to building a sound base of knowledge for field operations and product improvement. First, notes Bob Hicks, was a unit exchange program similar to that which was so effective with the T56/501: "The Army returned their engines here for overhaul for several years and we were able to do the same sort of inspection and preventive correction of things that might develop later on. I believe those programs succeeded largely because we were able to do our own in-house work and investigation before the engines were returned to service."

Second was an accident investigation program that ensured swift assessment of problem trends and early implementation of mechanical and operating improvements.

Small engine product line director George Mayo discussed the operation and safety associated with helicopters. He emphasized that the Allison organization remains an important element for the operator after the sale: "Helicopters often operate in high-risk environments—tough jobs, bad weather—and some owners working on

Above: Italy's Agusta A-109 twin-250 helicopter visited the Allison Division's Research and Development Center in 1976 as part of a sales demonstration tour. Capable of sustained cruise speeds up to 173 mph, the graceful, seven-passenger ship has a range of 335 miles and can climb 1,600 fpm on both engines, 300 fpm on one.

Right: German manufacturer Messerschmitt-Boelkow-Blohm (MBB) demonstrated its BO105 at Pike's Peak in 1985 by hovering on only one of its twin 500-hp 250-C28s.

near-shoestrings may take higher risks than they should. The total fleet of some 23,000 operational 250-powered aircraft experiences about five incidents per week, each of which generates a 'hot sheet' report.

"Accidents range from common to bizarre, but most are the same kinds of unremarkable things, from hooking a skid on a wire to rough-terrain tipovers. Elements contributing to helicopter accidents differ little from those associated with fixed-wing aircraft. They range from pilot-related factors through airframe and engine maintenance to powerplant operation. Our people often participate in investigations."

The Probable Cause

Small engine sales and product support manager Chuck Wagner became Allison's principal 250 investigator almost by default while working under corrective action department supervisor Bob Hatch, "probably the best failure analyst in the industry." Having conducted perhaps 85 percent of the early Model 250 accident investigations, Wagner provided revealing perspective about the engine and the company as well:

"Helicopters never go down in nice places, and they operate everywhere in the world—geological surveys, traffic reporting, firefighting, offshore oil rigs, air ambulance services, sightseeing, air taxis.

"For the accident investigator, there is always the challenge 'to beat the piece of iron,' to isolate an accident's probable cause so that it can be corrected. Experience and the essential details are the best tools. Always in the discovery process there is that sense of mutual trust shared in the aviation community—to identify and solve the problem."

The Blue Ribbon Campaign

Two significant trouble patterns emerged in early 250 field experience. The first occurred in the "light" helicopter application itself, among the most punishing in aviation. Early 250s operated close to maximum design limits throughout

Small engine product line director George Mayo worked on the T56/501, the industrial gas turbine project, and the TF41, before taking on his major role in the Model 250 program.

With over four decades of operation, Petroleum Helicopters, Inc. is the world's largest civilian operator of Allison's 250 engine. This five-place JetRanger returning from an offshore oil rig in the Gulf of Mexico was one of 126 of the type operated or on order by PHI in 1974.

When the 230-lb, 500-hp 250-C28B entered production in 1978, it expanded the helicopter designer's options of ship weight, payload, speed, and range. Modular design allows rapid replacement of major engine sections without disturbing adjacent components.

every flight. The second, for all the designers' work to control vibration from the outset, were recurrent gear failures and compressor blade fractures, both tracked to induced frequency vibration.

Allison created the Blue Ribbon Engine Campaign to systematically fix the engine's field-discovered problems. The blade cracking was solved with a program of regrinding the wheels in the field; and modifications to the drive train eliminated the gear difficulty. Bearing performance was a separate issue, and improved materials and design were required.

Market Growth

Mike Hudson recalls one impressive helicopter sales motivator: "For every problem in the world, there's an equal opportunity for someone else. The Arab oil embargo of 1973-74 generated major problems in parts of the economy, but it was a boom for us. Oil production blossomed, so helicopter business blossomed, and we [reached production] of 2,000 engines a year, with over 200 engines in some months. And spare parts just went off the charts as well."

Among the transport companies responding to the oil producers' surging demand was Petroleum Helicopters, Inc., of Lafayette, Louisiana. Founded in 1949 by the late Bob Suggs, PHI grew from three Model D Bells and 11 employees to become the largest firm of its kind in the world, employing 700 pilots, 800 mechanics, and 450 support staff worldwide. Surpassed only by the U.S. military as a single user of the 250, PHI's fleet of 350 'copters in 1987 averaged 21,000 hours per month. Its Allison turbines accumulated more than four million flight hours.

Sustained Leadership

In spring 1978 two uprated models of the 250 achieved certification: for Bell's LongRanger II, the 500 shp -C28B; for Sikorsky Aircraft's S-76, the 650 hp -C30.

The S-76 application particularly pleased Fred Egbert, Bill Castle, and their Allison engineering team. The 250's final competitor for that application had been the PT6 of Sikorsky's sister-company at United Technologies, Allison arch-rival Pratt & Whitney. A twin-engine, 12-place, five-ton aircraft, the S-76 was built to service the world's growing armada of offshore oil rigs. Turboprop applications for the 250 also began in the 1970s, notably by SIAI Marchetti and Partenavia in

Italy, Britten-Norman in Great Britain, and the Government Aircraft Factory in Australia.

Military upgrades continued to generate production. In 1977 the U.S. Army contracted to retrofit 500 OH-58A helicopters to OH-58C with the new 250-C20B (military T63-A-720), increasing power by 30 percent to meet expanded mission requirements. As growth variants were developed in the late 1970s, Model 250 engine production ranged from 1,500 to 2,000 units annually.

In the 1980s, the Army upgraded additional OH-58As to the OH-58D configuration, under the Army Helicopter Improvement Program (AHIP), using the 250-C30 (military T703).

Above: Among the principal managers of the Model 250 program in its formative development phase was Fred Egbert, the powerplant's chief engineer.

Left: Assembler Lester Wagoner completes pre-test work on a prototype Model 250-C-30 turboshaft in January 1977. The 650-hp unit was built for Sikorsky's S-76 helicopter then approaching production.

Below: Sikorsky Aircraft's S-76 twin-engine, 16-place, five-ton aircraft was built to service the world's growing armada of offshore oil rigs, primarily in the Gulf of Mexico and the North Sea.

Among turboprop applications of the 250 is the Nomad N24A produced by the Government Aircraft Factory in Australia, in both military and civilian versions.

Two key figures in Allison's rise to worldwide prominence in turbine engine technology retired in 1980. Norman Eggers (left), then sales manager for Indianapolis Operations, was instrumental in shaping the company's global sales and service network. Gordon Holbrook, director of research and engineering, shared in guiding development of the T56 (the engine in the rear), the TF41, and the Model 250 (foreground).

The T63/250 family has achieved the broadest application of any Allison engine in history, powering the aircraft of nearly 60 manufacturers. The largest single user by far is Bell, with almost half of some 24,000 engines.

The Distributor Network

However fine the engine, its enormous success among thousands of globally-dispersed operators would not have been possible without rigorously systematic product support and a competent and responsive distribution system.

The key, says George Mayo, is Allison's worldwide distributor network of nine independent aviation service companies, each of which has earned distinction in the industry apart from its Allison affiliation. Distributors provide the first line of support for the customers, including even the federal government, from pre-sale application analysis to training, parts and tool supply, maintenance, and overhaul. Distributor contracts are renewed on two- and three-year terms, and Allison management teams conduct annual, on-site engineering, quality, business and financial audits.

The Origins of Field Service

Allison's global network of commercial distributors emerged from a proud historic predecessor: the Allison field service organization created in 1940 for the U.S. Army Air Corps.

As Allison's V1710 engine programs had accelerated throughout World War II, the complex details of model changes, installation variations, production coordination, and operational and maintenance training required the closest imaginable coordination between the company and the Air Corps. The military and civilian leaders at Wright Field came to consider the Allison enterprise as a virtual civil extension of their operations.

From the very beginning, program managers recognized the merit of assigning Allison service representatives to the field wherever significant numbers of Allison-powered airplanes were to operate. As resourceful problem-solvers, the reps provided technical guidance, training, administrative support, and vital liaison between the company and the users of its sophisticated product.

And so Arne Butteberg and Tye Lett had gone to China with the Flying Tigers's Warhawks. Don Orme accompanied squadrons of Lightnings through the Middle East, North Africa, and Italy. Oscar Kaiser journeyed to Russia with the Airacobras and King Cobras. And Dick McKenna, still with Allison in 1990 after 53 years, worked with Britain's wartime Royal Air Force on all those aircraft, plus the Mustang.

As gas turbine engines replaced the V1710, liaison continued with the new U.S. Air Force and burgeoned with the Navy and Army, too. The magnitude of jet engine activity resulted in the establishment of a Washington Zone Office. Systematic and frequent contact between Allison reps and the armed services' offices at the Pentagon allowed the company to keep abreast of military requirements. From program development to operational problem-solving and contract negotiation, the Washington office has facilitated the company's successful government programs for many years.

The Allison field reps' contribution to the military mission did not go unrecognized. Among the many formal acknowledgements made of reps over the years was Dick Valley's Medal of Freedom in 1954 for his work with the F-89 Scorpion program in Korea. Larry Banks served four duty tours in wartime Vietnam, often working on T63-powered helicopters under fire, and was awarded the Civilian Commendation Medal.

Honored with the Civilian Commendation Medal, Allison Field Service representative Larry Banks served four duty tours in wartime Vietnam. In the background of this combat zone snapshot is a Cessna O-1A (L-19) Bird Dog Light Observation Aircraft.

Because Allison-built turbojets and turboprops powered so many operational and experimental airplanes built and tested in Southern California in the 1950s, the company established a Los Angeles Zone Office. Allison sales engineers were in daily contact with Lockheed, Douglas, and Northrop in Burbank, Hawthorne, Palmdale, Long Beach, and El Segundo. A San Diego office coordinated with Convair on that firm's seaplane and VTOL programs and the Turbo-Liner.

Other satellite offices were set up as needed. When the volume of test work—principally on B-45 and F3H aircraft and Regulus and Snark missiles—exceeded capacity at Plant 10 in Indianapolis, a separate cadre of service reps was assigned to Edwards AFB. A New York office supported Republic and Grumman on the E2 and C2 aircraft, and East Coast reps provided line support to Electra operators, especially American, National and Eastern airlines at Idlewild (later Kennedy), La Guardia, and Newark airports. In Marietta, Georgia, the Atlanta District office was established to support Lockheed's C-130 Hercules manufacture.

With worldwide Electra operations came the need for Allison service offices in Amsterdam and in Hong Kong. Military engine programs benefited from representation in Frankfurt and Tokyo. From Indianapolis between 1950 and 1979, Allison service on military programs around the world was managed by Len Davidson, Don Wright, and Ed Hatch.

Not All Helicopters Are Light, or Fly

For each company success, other often valiant efforts yield modest results. Sometimes the primary result is a bridge to another opportunity. Such an effort was the Army's heavy lift helicopter competition of the early 1970s.

Even without its propulsion machinery, Boeing Vertol's Heavy Lift Helicopter mockup presents an imposing sight. The airframe continued Vertol's tradition of long, twin-rotor designs, but the early-1970s program was cancelled by the Army before the prototype was fully developed.

The program called for a three-engine helicopter able to fly with 20 tons of payload with one engine out. Boeing Vertol was awarded the airframe development contract over Hughes and Sikorsky. Allison won the preliminary powerplant development and testing over GE.

The Army contract with Boeing provided for systems testing in an "iron bird" test stand that replicated the projected three-engine layout of the aircraft. Boeing asked Allison to use a two-shaft variant of the T56 in the 4,000-hp range, with the three engines driving into a huge gearbox of Boeing design.

Allison's contract bargaining with Boeing Vertol was itself unusual. Two days before Christmas 1973, the Indianapolis team of six—two from contracts, one each from sales, engineering, legal, and finance—went to Boeing Vertol's Philadelphia headquarters to negotiate. After the first long session, they returned to the hotel to refigure costs in light of additional things Vertol had requested. The team came back and bid the job for substantially more than the first offer—and still won.

Yet another exotic-looking test stand, the Dynamic System Test Rig (DSTR)—the "Iron Bird" of 1974—was built to test the operation of the Boeing HLH propulsion system. One of the 501-M62B turboshaft engines (similar to the XT701), its inlet shrouded with wire mesh, is mounted near the rig's center.

Discussing Allison's power package for the HLH at Boeing Vertol's Philadelphia plant in April 1972 were Boeing vice president and Vertol Division general manger Howard Stuverude (left), Detroit Diesel Allison Division general manager Jim Knott (center), and Boeing's HLH system branch manager Thomas P. Peppler.

The first flight-rated, 8,000-hp XT701 turboshaft engine for the Army's Boeing HLH was accepted by military contracts representative USAF Lt. Col. Tom Olofson on February 7, 1975. Marking the presentation were XT701 chief project engineer William Castle (left), and aircraft gas turbine engineering director Gordon Holbrook (center).

Winning meant more development on the engine, and delivery of five engines for the iron bird—three installed, two spares. While that phase was underway, the Army decided to compete the actual helicopter engines—the XT701 program—and again Allison won the development contract over GE.

The XT701 contract project was noteworthy as Allison's first with the design-to-cost award fee provision. The engine was to be designed with manufacturing costs calculated from day one and projected against specified production volumes. Allison earned 100 percent of the award fee for its efforts on the agreement, and the engine program came in on time as well. Then the contract was abruptly cancelled for both Boeing and Allison. Nonetheless, working with Boeing Vertol was a happy experience for all involved in the effort.

From Iron Bird to Heavy Industry

No successful manager neglects to apply developed technology from one to another suitable arena. The adaptation of the XT701 to the Model 570 for the commercial market illustrated such transfer perfectly.

Bob Hicks described the results: "Our Model 570 engine began [with] the heavy-lift helicopter, funded with some $30 to $40 million before the helicopter program was stopped. When the engine program ended, many people at Allison felt that we should pursue that engine so that we would not lose the very considerable knowledge acquired in its development. The decision was made to introduce the 7,000-eshp Model 570 as an industrial engine for gas compression, marine propulsion, and electrical power generation.

"In July 1979, the first production-configuration Model 570K industrial gas turbine engines were readied for shipment with minimal additional development work. Some engines being developed and sold in the 1990s, including the engine for the Osprey V-22, benefit tremendously from the experience and know-how we obtained on the Model 570."

Of even greater potential is the company's work on a subsequent project. In the 1977 Army competition for a high performance turboshaft demonstrator engine in the 800-hp class, Allison's development contract resulted in the GMA500 engine. This Advanced Technology Demonstrator Engine (ATDE) achieved precisely the high power-to-weight ratio and low SFC in a compact unit stipulated by the Army for its next generation of powerplants.

This program led into the T800 engine competition in 1985, in which Allison teamed with the Garrett Corporation to win one of two prototype development contracts. The 1200-hp-class engine is scheduled to power the Army's next-generation light helicopter (LH) and several others. Allison and Garrett will carry on development to a production powerplant. Subject to shifting U.S. defense priorities, the T800 engine program over the course of LH production is the largest Army aircraft procurement in the foreseeable future. Allison can anticipate significant commercial production of the basic engine.

Productive Detours

Allison's time-honored stories include several that recall not only Carl Fisher's zaniness of decades past but also the creativity of imaginative technology, if not great business. "The Breech Loader" of the mid-1960s is such a tale, pieced together here from versions shared by participants:

"At a cocktail party in Detroit in 1965, one of our senior people, perhaps Harold Dice or Dim Gerdan, was chatting with an Army general working on the joint U.S.-West German battle

The pre-prototype drawing of Allison's breech loader for the U.S.-West German MBT-70 tank provides some clues of the mechanism's sheer complexity. The array of chains, gears, pistons, and servos functioned with great reliability.

tank development. Said the general, 'We've got a tank breech loader with a one-cycle life: you shoot it and it blows up. Even the Germans can't make it work. Perhaps some of those people at Allison who do special things can help us!'

Unable to resist the challenge, our man said encouraging things that led to a contract. Repeated test failures had been an embarrassment to everybody, and there was great urgency to put the problem to rest.

"In only a few months, Al Short and project manager Hal Hensley designed a mechanism that automatically loaded one of four types of round selected by the gunner. It worked like a charm the first time and every time after. Even though we lost a bundle, it was a happy experience, setting the tone of Allison's capability to do strange and curious things." Production records show some 1,500 of the units were made between 1966 and 1968, at an average price of $7,500 each.

The Air Breathing Missiles

Among the branches of Allison's family tree of engine work are four relatively brief excursions into missiles and rocket propulsion that occurred between 1950 and 1959. The projects link the Pentagon's exploration of rocket-launched, air-breathing missiles as offensive weapons and Allison's production of J33 and J71 turbojets.

Earliest among the missiles came the Navy's carrier- and submarine-borne, Chance Vought XSSM-N-8 Regulus, powered by the J33-A-18 and first flown late in 1950. By

1959, 900 successful Regulus launches had been achieved. Next came the J71-powered Northrop SM-62 Snark for the U.S. Air Force, the first on-line intercontinental guided missile. The Snark first flew in August 1953. Last came two Army missiles powered by J33-A-37s: the Martin TM-61 Matador in June 1954; and the TM-76 Mace that was deployed in both Germany and Okinawa.

The Space Age

In the night sky of October 4, 1957, appeared the first earth-orbiting satellite, the Soviet Union's Sputnik I. Along with the epochal little space vehicle's impact on the relationships of nations came an immediate and galvanizing effect on the American aerospace industry.

Allison was not immune to the space bug. In 1958 the notion of implementing a missile systems function group circulated in Detroit and Indianapolis. It was reinforced by GM's own earlier exploration of possible entry into the weapons systems business. In the mid-1950s the corporation had looked for a weapons systems expert. They turned for advice to renowned space physicist James Van Allen who in December 1958 recommended Herb Karsch.

If at First . . .

Jim Knott recalls the corporation's early response to the new challenge when he was assistant director of engineering: "In 1958 we were looking for business. Cy Osborn, the GM executive vice president through whom we reported, urged us to bid on an RFP for a reentry body in cooperation with the AC Division in Milwaukee, which had skills and resources applicable to guidance systems. After Dim Gerdan and I conferred with AC's Chuck Skinner, I listed all the things I thought we needed to know, and made assignments to engineers, most of whom had never worked on such a product. We teamed up with RCA, bid, and lost. But our appetite had been whetted."

Facing page, top: The Army's J33-powered TM-61 Martin Matador had a range of 600 miles at a speed of 600 mph, and was widely deployed in Europe.

Facing page, bottom: The Navy's carrier and submarine-borne Chance Vought XSSM-N-8 Regulus, powered by the J33-A-18, was built in two versions — a tactical missile and a recoverable model that could be tested and retrieved repeatedly. Wheeled carts permitted quick launches from the carrier deck.

Above: The J71-powered Northrop SM-62 Snark was the Air Force's first on-line intercontinental guided missile and could deliver an atomic warhead over trans-oceanic distances.

An important contributor to Allison's aerospace activity was Plant 8 rocket motor research laboratory project engineer Gus Broffitt.

Allison's ventures into rocket technology provided new vistas of sophisticated practical research. Engineer Fred Short prepares to photograph deflected light that reveals rocket nozzle internal air flow. The goal was "contour optimization" that would permit exhaust flow at maximum velocity.

The Flawless Rocket Cases

The next aerospace effort paid off with dividends both in technical advances and in profitable business during an otherwise financially trying period. The project was rocket motor cases, and Allison's introduction was chancy indeed. Clarence Perry tells the story:

"In 1958 I went to Washington with our sales department personnel to bid on the second stage Thiokol rocket motor case for the Minuteman missile. When I got to Washington, the 44-inch-diameter second stage case had already been contracted, so I bid on the 60-inch first stage. When we got back to Indianapolis, everyone was pleased that we'd gotten the contract . . . except Mr. Dice [then general manager]. He said, 'I told you we couldn't handle the 60-inch job. You've gotten us in the soup, now you get us out.' I searched the country for equipment big enough to handle the 60-inch case and found what we needed right at the Cleveland Tank Plant. The five prototypes were very successful and led to a contract for several hundred, plus the facility contract that allowed us to buy large lathes and put a lot of business in Plant 8, which needed it at that time."

Thiokol was the prime contractor for manufacturing both cases and solid propellant. They were competent chemical people, recall engineers familiar with the program, but not experts on hardware. Allison's success in the subcontract bidding on the lightweight steel cases derived from the design of a threaded joint—much like a huge Mason jar—as opposed to a bolted joint.

Part of the new Plant 8 gas turbine research facility was modified as a rocket motor research laboratory. The team began with inhouse staff. Then roving recruiting teams sought out the needed specialists—talented engineers and scientists with advanced degrees and experience. Nuclear physicist Tibor Nagey, who became director of research, was hired in June 1958 from the Glenn L. Martin Company. Gus Broffitt was named project engineer.

The first Minuteman case passed its acceptance test on March 2, 1959, and a complete missile was fired successfully on the first launch attempt in February 1961.

Allison continued to build its high tech reputation over a wide spectrum of contract projects in the 1960s. In May 1960 the company was selected by the Atomic Energy Commission as one of two contractors to develop a compact nuclear powerplant for Army field units to produce power in dispersed locations. By early 1962 Allison Research activity was solidly established with major funding provided by military departments, scientific agencies, and GM.

From programs aimed at flight propulsion in and outside the atmosphere, Allison obtained U.S. development rights for the Stirling engine that employs a 150-year-old principle of a work cycle brought up to modern standards by N.V. Philips Gloeilampenfabrieken Works in Holland. The powerplant has the capacity to obtain energy from any heat source and run unattended for as long as two years.

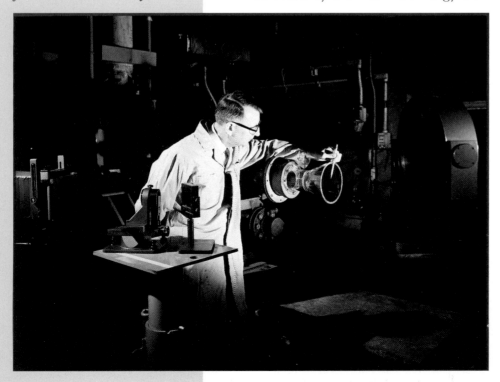

The Stirling-cycle external combustion engine offered attractive power options for satellites and manned space stations. Engineers J. Paul Miller (left) and Donald Monson check external hardware on a test engine that had just completed 1,000 hours of endurance running in Plant 8 in summer 1963.

Reviewing the technology of the Stirling engine (a laboratory model is on the table) in September 1959 are research director Tibor Nagey (right) and advanced weapons systems project manager Herbert Karsch. Nagey supervised some of Allison's most advanced research. Karsh played leadership roles in many Allison programs, including the TF41 engine.

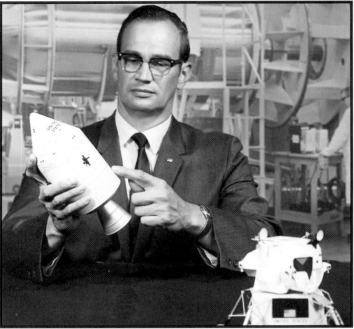

Assistant chief engineer Jack Patten uses a model of the Apollo 11 service and command modules to locate the Allison-built propellant tanks that contributed to the success of the first manned lunar landing. That dramatic Apollo 11 mission ran from July 16 to July 24, 1969.

When Allison was chosen for production of the rocket motor cases, the project shifted from the research department to its own unit, the Rocket Engine Activity. That consolidation gave Allison aerospace work the strength of integrated research and development, tooling, and manufacturing teams.

The results were gratifying. In building more than 800 first and second stage motor cases, Allison had not a single failure in tests. In contrast, GE and other manufacturers had multiple failures, even when making the cases to Allison design.

During a lean time for gas turbine engine work, the fortuitous rocket business flourished to sustain the division. Said Jim Knott: "Our Minuteman work got us into rocket nozzle business with the Titan IIIC, and our thin-wall case reputation led to manufacturing the fuel tanks for the Apollo Lunar Excursion Module and the Command Module (beginning in 1961; the last Apollo flight was in 1975) under subcontract to Grumman and North American."

However, when General Electric was awarded the major rocket motor case manufacturing follow-on contract with a bid of $500 per unit below theirs, Allison managers chose to quit the rocket motor business.

Meanwhile, in Detroit

As the 1970s approached, the Allison Division was about to begin a struggle for its very existence, a struggle perhaps inevitable from the day the men of General Motors had determined to acquire Jim Allison's company four decades earlier.

Below: Precise control of the welding process for the USAF Minuteman that mated sections into a 22-foot-long case contributed to the failure-free Allison record maintained throughout the program's life. The Minuteman's spectacularly successful maiden flight in February 1961 was also the first free flight of Allison's first stage rocket motor case.

Facing page: During 1961 Plant 8 inspectors became accustomed to larger products than usual. Engineer Ralph Green (lower right) supervises examination of three units. At left a 24-ft rocket motor case dwarfs two rocket propellant storage tanks. The experimental tank at the right is made of spun fiberglass. Courtesy Ralph Green.

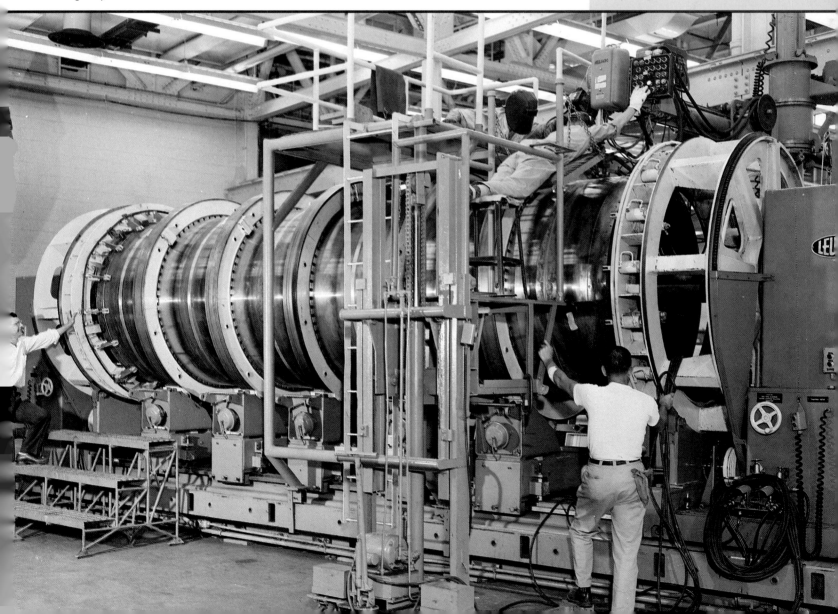

CHAPTER 10
Challenging

The Allison/Detroit Diesel merger;
corporate and division perspectives;
autos and alternatives.
Turbines on the road.
Lean times; on the block a second time.
It's worth doing: Blake Wallace,
independence, teams, a strategy.
Allison, LHX, and the T800.
Turbines for industry.
Tomorrow's turboprops; the Saab 2000.
The Technology Frontier; GM Synergy
Facing the Future.

Previous page: Intended to provide high mobility in limited landing areas, the Navy's Bell Boeing V-22 Osprey is powered by two Allison T406 turbo-props. The tilt rotor configuration combines the vertical lift capability of the helicopter and the high speed of fixed wing aircraft.

Below: By May 1971 the cosmetics of merger were largely in place. Maywood's Plant 5 sign was changed by sign company workers James Elliott (left), and Ira Combs, supervised by Oscar Wacker, Jr. (in coat). The revised version of the former Detroit Diesel Engine Division's "Spinning Arrows" logo denoted both the rotating power of engines and transmissions and the joining of Allison's Indianapolis operations with the former Detroit Diesel Engine Division.

The September 1, 1970, news release said: "GM chairman James M. Roche announced the consolidation of Detroit Diesel Engine Division with Allison. The new organization, Detroit Diesel Allison Division, is headquartered in Detroit.

"James E. Knott, GM vice president and former Allison general manager, has been named general manager of the new division. Knott said Detroit Diesel has an immediate and long-range need for additional diesel engine capacity that can be met with Allison floor space available at Plants 5 and 2, with more becoming available during the next few years. It should not be necessary to build any new floor space, while at the same time Plant 5 will manufacture diesel engine parts, he pointed out.

"Detroit Diesel's beginning line of industrial gas turbines will be accelerated and expanded, and we plan that Indianapolis Operations will become the industrial gas turbine development center for GM. We have the technical and manufacturing experience, as well as test facilities.

"The merger brings under one manager the diesel engines and transmissions which are extremely successful in industrial and off-the-road applications and are frequently installed as a package. Both product lines are profitable and the market is expanding, he said. The merger will provide the added sales volume and individual security that Allison needs, Mr. Knott said."

Turbines, Pistons, High Hopes

That terse announcement reflected the optimistic intent of the corporate planners in Detroit. But for all its seeming merit in 1970, the yoking together of three separate businesses—gas turbines, diesel engines, and heavy-duty transmissions— contained the makings of its own undoing.

During the decade to follow, distinct market factors governing each of the three businesses required management strategy and tactics increasingly at odds with one another. The divergence was not immediate, and new division teammates tackled their fresh problems with determination.

Most Allison veterans of the era of the Detroit Diesel Allison Division from 1970 to 1983 were pleased that it ended with division independence for the gas turbine operation.

The DDA Rationale

Driven by practical considerations that seemed desirable in 1969, senior corporate planners assessed circumstances at GM's Detroit Diesel Division and Allison Operations. From some perspectives, sound factors favored a merger, recalls one senior Gas Turbine executive. The booming diesel engine market was straining Detroit Diesel's production capacity in Michigan; major diesel engine customers were actually on allocation. Studies showed that new plant costs would make production unprofitable.

Some observers in the turbine shop felt that because of dwindling markets the division was headed out of business. A significant portion of Allison manufacturing capacity was under-utilized. More factory space, it was anticipated, would soon become available in Indianapolis. The Model 250 engine had troubles, they said; the T56/501 could not go on; the TF41 was just a bonanza.

Detroit Diesel's general manager was about to retire. In Allison's Jim Knott they saw a skilled and practical manager whose career had proven a gutsy blend of engineering savvy, business common sense, and willingness to take on tough challenges. Diesels and transmissions were compatible products and some diesel parts were already being manufactured by Allison. In Indianapolis, Detroit saw a proven engineering and manufacturing team, a seasoned work force of intelligent and loyal people, and . . . floor space.

An Uneasy Beginning

The view from Maywood by the following spring was more complex. From their earliest GM association, the aviation-oriented gas turbine staff had enjoyed a spirited independence and unique status. Suddenly their long-term and daily priorities were weighed with those of diesel engines and transmissions. Certainly Detroit Diesel's large volume and expanding markets consumed a large portion

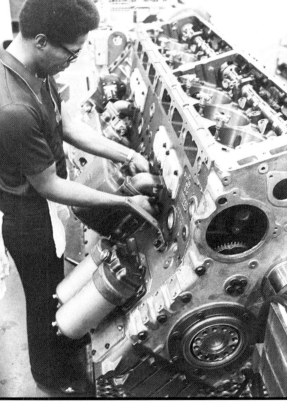

of management attention, but attitudes toward the change were shaped as much by perception as fact.

As they had since 1915, Allison's people met the Detroit challenge with competence, flexibility, and energy. In September 1975 the 3,000th Series 149 diesel engine to be built in Indianapolis since 1973 neared completion. Assembler Price Petty, Jr. (left) fits a cooling system component to the block of the 12-cylinder, 1,000-hp unit destined for an 85-ton mining truck. James Lloyd (above) lowers the unit to a dolly for transport to final assembly and test.

The mood of the new organization's early months lingers in the recollections of Allison veterans. Says one, "We felt that more Diesel people came out on top than Allison people. Much like the Dayton folks from Aeroproducts before, we felt we'd been taken into an us-versus-them environment with the larger partner dominating." Another reflects,

Jim Knott began his career as a flight engineer and spent much of his Allison energy on aeronautical engineering. But it was his reputation as a strong, practical manager that earned him the assignment of general manager of the consolidated operations of the Detroit Diesel Allison Division in September 1970.

The range of DDA's transport product applications covered vivid extremes. Painstakingly pared of every extraneous inch and ounce, Allison's Model 250 turboshaft helicopter engine (left) compressed its 400 hp into 159 lbs. Less constrained by weight and size requirements, the company's 325-hp GT-404 gas turbine engine for trucks, busses, and stationery applications weighed about 1,700 lbs.

"We redirected discretionary funds into the truck engine. Our top management strength—the men who knew the aircraft business, Jim Knott, Don Atwood—was intent on internal reorganization. They were grappling with the issues confronting Detroit Diesel: production capacity for commercial engines, and the like."

Turbines for the Road

"The truck engine" refers to a project that had been shuttled to and from Detroit with fluctuating expectations—a gas turbine engine intended for highway, marine, and industrial applications to compete with gasoline and diesel power.

Allison's first skirmish with vehicular gas turbines came in the late 1950s when the GMT305 engine program was moved from General Motors Research Laboratories to Allison for further development. GMR had pioneered a series of prototype vehicular gas turbine engines beginning in 1950, powering Firebird race cars, GM trucks, and other potential corporate products. Deciding to advance the engine into full-scale engineering development, GM chose Allison for the job.

Intended to compete with gasoline and diesel engines, the GMT305 produced about 300 hp and incorporated a regenerative cycle for better SFC than typical simple-cycle turbines. Allison improved the engine, and built 16 prototype units in 1958 and 1959 for lease to manufacturers to evaluate in the field. Installations included a heavy-duty ore hauler truck, a highway truck tractor, an Army M56 gun carrier and four-wheel drive tractor, two amphibious resupply vehicles, and three test-bed rigs at oil companies.

While much was learned in various field test periods, no project led to production. The program moved from GM Research to Detroit Diesel, and in 1971 returned to Indianapolis, where development work continued on a powerplant family—the GT404 (300 hp), 505 (400 hp), and 605 (500 hp).

General Motors and Allison invested something like $250 million in the engine's 300-hp version. Although the GT404 became a primary component of the generator set for the U.S. Army Patriot missile system deployed in Europe, several factors prevented its finding a commercial market.

Plans had called for the 404's commercial introduction when it was only 20 percent less fuel efficient than comparable diesels, but then came OPEC and the winter of 1973-74. The fuel crunch sank the GT family.

The U.S. Army found the GT-404-4 an ideal component for its mobile Patriot ground-to-air guided missile system. Combined with a Delco-built 150-kilowatt alternator, the 300-hp, 1,800-lb gas turbine generated the electrical power for the system's intricate computer guidance and control systems. The first of some 230 units was delivered in December 1981.

The economics of initial cost and fuel consumption for on-highway turbines have not yet seriously challenged conventional gasoline and diesel engines. But Allison's gas turbines of the 1970s offered outstanding vehicle performance, especially when combined with suitable automatic power transmission. The GT-404 was tested extensively over the road in experimental installations such as this tilt-cab GMC tractor, and intercity buses.

Hard economics haven't entirely erased fond memories of the smooth and immensely powerful engines that turned prototype buses into true Greyhounds and more than one big rig into a blue ox.

Again, Two Cultures

There was a clear sense after Jim Knott became general manager of the consolidated Detroit Diesel Allison, with so much of his time spent over in the diesel side of the house, that Indianapolis did not get an equal share of management attention.

Following Knott, general managers Don Atwood, Pete Smith, and Lud Koci felt more comfortable with their prior worlds in GM than the unique one of Allison. The emphasis in Maywood favored industrial and truck gas turbines and diesel components. Advanced aero-oriented gas turbine technology continued through government R&D programs, but new product development slowed.

At the heart of the growing unease felt by the turbine people lay basic differences. The two central and incompatible issues were: the development efforts gas turbine veterans knew were necessary to build and maintain a meaningful role in the jet engine industry, and the dominant focus on manufacturing that drove so much GM behavior.

The differences were of both substance and of degree. Many Allison people themselves did not fully grasp the continuing technology and demanding effort needed to remain competitive with General Electric and Pratt & Whitney.

The General Motors attitude came not only from the realities of the automobile, but the accountant's "bottom line" evidence so hard to counter with often-expensive engineering futures. Allison, after all, in the post-WWII decade had built 92 percent of all jet engines in this country. In 1952, for example, 6,600 J33 and J35 engines had flowed down the assembly line—remarkably like Roadmasters, Stylelines, and Rockets—with income nearing a billion dollars. A corporate urge to repeat that performance is easy to understand.

The Allison aero engine team saw clearly that in Washington and Dayton, in Cincinnati and East Hartford, that old order no longer held.

It wasn't holding in Indianapolis, either, but the proof that finally galvanized Detroit came not from Allison, but from a prospective joint venture partner and a seemingly coincidental remark.

As new military engine opportunities arose in 1981, Garrett AiResearch Corporation approached GM's corporate people to explore joint venturing. GM group vice president Reuben Jensen allegedly suggested, "Why don't you just buy Allison?"

On the Block Again

If one buyer was interested, why not test the market?

In April 1982 came this announcement from Detroit: "While DDAD-Gas Turbine has been an attractive source of earnings through the years, General Motors has determined to explore the sale of the business in order to raise capital for employment in its core automotive operations." The text continued, "DDAD-Gas Turbine has become known for excellent manufacturing facilities, a high degree of engineering expertise; strong research, development, and testing capabilities; good relationships with the Government through its numerous manufacturing and engineering contracts; and safe, reliable, quality products."

The copy didn't exactly sizzle, but seven possible buyers contacted GM about buying Allison, including Harold Gray at United Technologies, TRW, Rolls-Royce, even a seven-member Indianapolis syndicate.

Suddenly, the gas turbine operation was to be examined in an appropriate and adequate context. To many insiders, the process began awkwardly, the cold scrutiny of strangers. It was uncomfortable, even threatening. For several months prospective buyers poked and probed. The investment house of Morgan Stanley was brought in to survey and evaluate. Sums up one department head, "Everyone was telling us about our business, and the whole thing was bad news."

The gloom-sayers could not have been more wrong. As Jensen and his boardroom colleagues watched and listened, they began to hear pointedly from strangers what they'd long resisted from their Indiana family.

Garrett made the high offer but it was patently unacceptable. However, the advice from the Morgan Stanley analysts was worth whatever was paid. If GM chose to stay in the business, they said, "First you ought to hire somebody who knows something about the turbine engine business to run it."

A Detroit View

John Debbink, whose 36-year GM career included the power products group vice presidency, 25 years with the Chevrolet Division, and general managerships of the Delco Moraine and Inland divisions, observed the DDA episode at close quarters and conversed regularly with the key participants. His observations are useful:

"When Allison Gas Turbine was recognized as having a distinctive product line and distinctive market, they were separated from the then-existing Detroit Diesel Allison Division. Gas turbines, like the transmission operation, depend on superior technology to succeed. High technology of an order well beyond most parts of the automobile business

Reuben R. Jensen was Allison's general manager from 1967 to 1969. As a GM group vice president, Jensen later played a significant role in the decisions which "unmerged" the Allison divisions from Detroit Diesel and set them on the road to autonomous operation.

John D. Debbink, who retired as power products group vice president in 1985, was among the senior GM executives in Detroit who strongly endorsed independent status for the Allison divisions in Indianapolis.

is required. Again, they must have a product superior for their niche in the market. They must have superior technology but also have to be very astute from the business standpoint. Major marketing efforts are required to be successful.

"In the past, we were trying to run an aircraft engine business with automotive people. There has been a maturing in the perspective from Detroit of what was going on in Indianapolis in the last five years, the comprehension that these people were in special businesses and should not be managed exactly like automotive businesses. They need to have the responsibility and authority of their own position to deal effectively with the competition in their market. They get battered by their own cycle plus they get battered by the cycles of the automotive business— with capital constraints and all the other pressures of times of downturn. They've been well supported, but should be able to play in their own ballpark. If the two divisions were not part of GM, they would shine out as outstanding companies. But being a part of a giant, they don't get that kind of recognition."

Donald J. Atwood (left) was manager of Allison Indianapolis operations in 1970, then returned as DDA general manager and GM vice president from 1978 to 1981. On special assignment from his duties as general director of engineering and marketing, Bob Hicks (right) directed a key study that helped to convince GM management of Allison's enormous potential in the gas turbine marketplace.

First, Hesitant, Steps

Says the man who became the new division's first general manager, "The turning point was 1982 when possible sale of the gas turbine division was being considered for sale by GM. They decided not to because they couldn't get their price. They elected to stay in the business. Suddenly the operation got the visibility it hadn't had. They realized that if they didn't do something, the company would not grow. To stay in business, they had to do it better. Allison, under the direction of Bob Hicks, had made a strategic plan that called for reinvestment in new products and modernization, and directed the company toward concentration on shaft engines."

Central to that plan was a keen knowledge and understanding of jet engine realities. From a financial view, much of the plan's wisdom came from one man, comptroller Bill Skelton. For 20 years he was perhaps the most influential man in the financial department. Although he became assistant comptroller for Detroit Diesel, his heart was really in the gas turbine business. Bill protected the gas turbine people, to the best interest of the corporation as well as the division.

New Division, New Leadership

Reuben Jensen and his advisors had done their homework, and, taking their consultants' advice literally, had surely hired "somebody who knows something about the turbine engine business to run it." Their man was Blake Wallace, a native Arizonan who graduated from the California Institute of Technology in 1955 and earned his M.S. and Ph.D. at Arizona State University. In what he calls "the grand tour," Wallace had already worked for the "other three" of the Big Four of U.S. jet engine manufacturing—as a preliminary design engineer for Pratt & Whitney, as chief engineer of advanced technology at Garrett

Because of his career-long familiarity with the financial side of Allison operations and management, and his deep concern for the division and its people, DDA assistant comptroller Bill Skelton played a central role in planning the new independent Gas Turbine Division.

AiResearch, and manager of advanced technical plans and programs at General Electric.

When Wallace arrived in 1983, he said, "If we're going to be in this business, we not only need to excel in our current markets, but we must also reenter the major market sectors of fighters and large transports." That had been said—but not heard—before.

Positive response to their new status and their new leader crackled through Maywood like the pace car on Race Day.

Integrated Support

Blake Wallace speaks with an easy assurance when he recounts his own experience since arriving in Indianapolis: "The support from the corporation during these seven years has been everything they told me it would be and more. GM has let us set our own strategy and run our own business to a remarkable degree. I have more autonomy in running this business than my counterparts at Pratt or GE. And we've gone out and done what we said we were going to do."

The Whole Team

Just as vital as building a strong and flexible communications web among the division's managers and engineers has been the refinement of similar channels to the rest of the Allison team—organized labor, the scientific and academic communities, the customers, and the general public.

Those channels remain a high priority with Blake Wallace: "We must have a people-oriented philosophy that recognizes the extreme skill of our work force and develop the men and women involved in every phase of our business. We must constantly take the initiative, and that particularly includes smooth relations with labor, the pro-active assistance from and cooperation with our union leadership.

Dave Fenwick, President of United Auto Workers Local 933 is quick to agree: "Through the mid-1970s," he notes, "an adversarial situation existed between labor and management. By 1977 we began to see the developing worldwide competition—the Japanese, the Europeans all making transmissions and engines—and we decided that the union has to become a full partner in running the company. The old adversarial role was easy—we just shot at one another—but we were just destroying the labor base, and the company.

"The split into two divisions helped because we can deal directly with our own senior managers, where before only Detroit could make the big decisions. It's a lot better. Dr. Wallace, a terrific salesman, has built this division so we can compete in the world market. Now we're all in this fight for [economic] survival. The company has shown great concern for its people, and both Wallace and Clark have demanded the best. Now fully persuading our workers is the next key step. Otherwise, it's outsourcing our jobs. Five years from now will tell the story."

A cornerstone of the new Gas Turbine Division's forward thrust is the active participation of organized labor in the comprehensive management team. Typifying labor leadership's commitment to making Allison competitive in the new world marketplace is United Auto Workers Local 933 president David Fenwick.

Blake Wallace's Eight Steps

In March 1983 Blake Wallace was named general director of engineering and marketing. By May the decision was made to separate gas turbines out as an autonomous division. In September the separation occurred and Wallace was made the first general manager of the Allison Gas Turbine Division. In his own words, these are the basic strategies Wallace initiated.

First came an organizational philosophy. We had been run as a functional organization, with managers reporting to Detroit and Detroit Diesel. We elected to set up a matrix organization, not unlike that of other engine companies, with product line managers who integrate the activities of their programs as well as function managers (engineering and product support, for example).

Second, we established a product plan to strengthen and expand ourselves in the three market segments: light helicopters, large turboprops, and industrial and marine engines.

Having served an almost textbook apprenticeship with the "other three" of America's four leading turbine aero engine builders, Blake Wallace was selected in March 1983 to head Allison gas turbine operations. The following September he was named general manager and a GM vice president.

And for the longer term, the plan moved towards commercial transport engines and aimed to re-enter the high performance military engine business in the late 1990s.

Third, we emphasized a technology strategy, to continue an excellent tradition of a strong engineering department but with strengthened product development so that we could mature an engine before it reaches the field.

We also decided to reenter the advanced military engine R&D area, particularly the Advanced Turbine Engine Gas Generator (ATEGG) series of programs that we'd dropped out of. These programs provide both the basic technology and the building blocks for development of new, high performance engines.

Fourth, we implemented a product development strategy to fix the extant problems on existing products, make derivative products for near terms, then to establish a series of new engines.

Fifth, we tackled marketing. We rebuilt both quantitatively and in skills, largely from existing staff, mostly engineers. Marketing is as demanding a task as building an engineering or factory organization.

Sixth, we strengthened Product Support—what's called at GM, "service"—and centralized the functions of spare parts, training, and customer support in one area. Our distributor organization works well with us, drawing on the best of GM's practices.

Seventh, we've focused on manufacturing modernization and integration. Our first task was to make a manufacturing plan, then assemble the skills to generate one.

Eighth, we've built an independent finance and personnel staff here, a capability previously provided by the corporation. Recognize that personnel and finance are the primary communication departments within the organization.

Old Strengths, New Applications

Wallace's clear road map was drawn on the base of the original strategic plan to achieve and maintain preeminence in three market segments of the gas turbine business—large turboprops, industrial and marine engines, and light helicopters.

The Series IV T56/501 and its parallel industrial engines, along with the 571, continued to expand application potential for larger aero powerplants and in the industrial markets. From standby power generation for communications systems to a petroleum industry whose outlook was dramatically altered in August 1990, prospective demand for industrial turbines is likely to remain strong. Customers recognizing their superior power-to-weight ratios and reliability in comparison to piston engines continue to migrate to turbines.

Expanding Versatility for the 250

Providing the third solid market foundation was Allison's family of the Model 250 turboshaft engines. In addition to its commanding presence in the light and medium helicopter field, the Model 250 found important—and intriguing—new applications.

Bell Helicopter selected the 250-C30 in 1988 to power its Model 222 back into production as the 230. Not only did the C30 offer better performance and higher reliability than other manufacturers' candidate powerplants, but it allowed the re-engining of 222s to the new standard in a conversion option by Heli-Air, Inc. The kit provides power increases of 10 percent in hot-day rating and 15 percent in cruise.

In a major international breakthrough, early in 1990 the Model 250 engine was selected by the USSR's Kamov Design Bureau to power its Model 226 helicopter, a twin-engine version of the earlier Kamov 126. The new twin will be used for agriculture and utility purposes. The Russians selected the C20B on the basis of durability, reliability, and worldwide service availability. Significantly, the Kamov 226 will be FAA certified and offered for sale internationally.

George Mayo, director of small aircraft engines, notes that with the Model 250's international utilization, 11 flight hours are added to the total every minute. Mayo said, "The key to the Model 250's success has been our continual infusion of new technology into the basic engine. By kitting these upgrades, we keep older engines current and keep them flying.

"For example, a 250-C20R, an upgrade for the popular C20B, has been available since 1988. Agusta, McDonnell Douglas, and Bell have been selling helicopters with the C20R engine as standard equipment. Aerospatiale is completing certification of a C20R-powered AS355 Twin Star.

"The rotor craft business will continue to be good in the 1990s. The decade ahead will have strong opportunities, especially in the civil sector," concluded Mayo.

The LHX Team

The company's preeminent position in helicopter engines was underscored when, in October 1988, the U.S. Army Aviation Systems Command selected the team of Allison and Garrett AiResearch to develop engines for the LHX helicopter program. The $207 million contract was for qualification testing of the Army's T800 engine over a 30-month period.

Potential production contracts for the Army's requirement of 5,000 engines and spares have been projected to exceed $2 billion. Recent world events may alter that projection yet again.

GM executive vice president and head of the automotive components, power products, and defense operations groups, Bill Hoglund has been instrumental in shaping the corporation's vigorously constructive support for the Gas Turbine Division. Said Hoglund to the press early in 1990, "I see nothing but strong opportunity for Allison Gas Turbine over the longer term."

In Indianapolis the Army's decision was greeted with glee. The initial evaluation of the engines for LHX had been called the most competitive engine procurement process ever undertaken by the Department of Defense.

Allison and Garrett had formed the Light Helicopter Turbine Engine Company (LHTEC) to develop and produce the T800. At the time of the Army selection, in fact, LHTEC's T800 had already undergone more than 7,000 hours of testing and completed its preliminary flight rating.

The Department of Defense and the Army had made teaming a prerequisite of the competition. However, in a unique twist, the two major engine companies—Allison and Garrett—would cooperate on initial joint production but would then compete with each other for a share of future Army orders. The major benefit of this new approach was to provide the service with two competitive engine suppliers for the life of the program.

The T800 was a major advancement in helicopter engines. Rated at 1,200-1,300 shp and capable of growth without change in its frame size, the T800 was designed with a highly durable centrifugal-type compressor that was a major foreign object damage (FOD) deterrent. Over the life of the Army's helicopter experience, FOD had been a major source of

Allison has historically benefitted from astute partnerships in turbine engine development, most recently with Garrett AiResearch in the Light Helicopter Turbine Engine Company to jointly develop the ultra-sophisticated T800 helicopter engine. Visiting a T800 test stand are, from left, Joe Byrd, Pat Hurley (Garrett), Mal Craig (Garrett), Mike Hudson, and Blake Wallace.

helicopter down time. In addition, the T800 engine offered a 15-30 percent lower SFC and 25-40 percent more power for its size than current engines operated in the 800-1600-shp class.

In October 1988 Italy's Agusta flight tested their A129 with twin T800-power. It was the T800's first flight. Using fully automated digital engine controls (FADEC), the A129 rotorcraft provided the LHTEC team its initial "real world flight experience."

Expanding on T800 applications, the LHTEC team reached agreement with the U.S. Coast Guard to conduct a "proof of concept" flight test demonstration of a HH-65 helicopter equipped with two T800 engines.

Having imposed operating restrictions as a result of LTS101 engine failures on its HH-65A helicopter, early in 1990 the Coast Guard announced that it would evaluate LHTEC T800 engines as a potential replacement for its Aerospatiale HH-65A helicopters. The 20-month contract is intended to evaluate the ability of the T800 engine to enhance the helicopter's future readiness, availability, and capability. The evaluation is scheduled to be completed by mid-1991.

A major advantage of the USCG test to the Army is that it will provide early operational data on T800 powerplants. In addition, of course, the engine can enhance the Coast Guard's HH-65 lifesaving capability.

Late in 1989 the LHTEC team announced that T800 engines will be installed in a Westland Helicopter Battlefield Lynx. Scheduled for first flight in mid-1991, the Lynx is another international application to demonstrate the rugged simplicity of the T800. The Battlefield Lynx will perform with improved speed and agility because of the more powerful and responsive engines.

They Don't Just Fly

Jim Lunsford, industrial applications product line director, may be the ideal spokesman for the "new division," reflecting great enthusiasm and the kind of results the post-1983 independence has helped to produce:

"In 1983 the Gas Turbine folks welcomed independence. Blake asked me to head up the industrial product line, assuring me that I could run it as a business in total. The market has three parts: power generation, gas compression, and marine generators or boat power. Each product line allowed plenty of independence.

"Our business, perhaps 12 to 15 percent of the division's, is to take aircraft engines and put them into the industrial market, already defined. Our future challenge is to balance the variables. First is hoping that the right aero derivative engine happens to ring down in the right power size. The 501 and the 571 have been compatible, but our new ones may not meet upward power drift needs. It takes five to ten years and lots of money to develop an engine, and the business level of the industrial market makes it hard to justify dedicated new development. But we have the living technology that our competitors don't have. The question for a given market is not can we do it, but should we do it."

The industrial and aero environments provide interesting contrasts, not the least being the common industrial practice of simply turning on the engine and running it flat out at maximum continuous power for 15,000-20,000 hours. Allison is an industry leader in gas turbine electrical power generation. The division is also dominant in the marine field, both for propulsion in patrol boats and electrical power supply. Marinized 501s are the electrical power source aboard several classes of destroyers and cruisers. Three turbines are fitted, two for power, one for backup.

Above: The 2,745-shp 501-K14 gas turbine serves as an ideal powerplant for industrial gas compression and power generation applications. Coupled through a gear reduction box to a 4,160-volt generator, this unit took shape in Indianapolis for service with American Telephone & Telegraph Company at Wayne, Pennsylvania.

During the 1970s, the 501 engine attracted Boeing Aerospace Company's Naval systems Division to power their JetFoil boats. The 90-ft, 106-ton **Madeira,** *was delivered to the Far East Hyrdofoil Company for the Hong Kong-Macao passenger route. A pair of 501s drove high-pressure pumps that expelled 45,000 gallons per minute to move the 284-passenger boats up to 50 mph. Boeing later sold its hydrofoil operations to Japan's Kawasaki Heavy Industries.*

An Important Core Engine, the T406

Allison, following its long tradition of turboprop engines, in the mid-1980s developed and produced the T406-AD-400. The prototype advanced turboprop was tested in mid-1988 in Allison's Indianapolis prop-tunnel facility. Its initial application is the U.S. Navy's V-22 Osprey tiltrotor aircraft. *(see page 172.)*

The V-22 application required another of Allison's inventive test stands. The all-attitude rig, with engine mounted, travels a 205-degree arc to position the engine anywhere from 90 degrees nose down through

115 degrees "over the top" and nose up. The stand was built to demonstrate that the T406 can provide lubrication systems in aircraft engines that must tilt from horizontal to vertical positions and back again while airborne.

Frank Verkamp, director of product programs, summarized the engine that has already provided the foundation for many promising programs: "A T406-based turboprop, scheduled to be qualified for production in 1991, will be 30 percent more fuel efficient and 19 percent more powerful than existing turboprops. The T406 engine and gearbox arrangement is based on Allison's proven experience with our T56. It is compatible with the P-3, E-2/C-2, and C-130 installations as well as future civil short-haul feeder aircraft. Including fly-by-wire FADEC, the T406 engine for the V-22 has already powered three of these versatile tilt-rotor aircraft for the military services."

The astonishing events of August 1990 adjacent to the Persian Gulf compelled yet another radical reassessment of assumptions about global strategies for peace and war. Whatever course U.S. policy may take, flexible battlefield tactics that require swift mobility--and machines like the V-22--seem likely to remain a priority for some time.

The turbine's quiet operation was one factor in its selection by the U.S. Navy to provide electricity and compressed air for its 30 Spruance-class destroyers. Each of the 563-ft ships, built at Pascagoula, Mississippi, by Ingalls Shipbuilding, carries three 501-K17s in generator sets fabricated by DDA distributor Stewart & Stevenson of Houston, Texas. The U.S.S. Caron is based at Norfolk, Virginia.

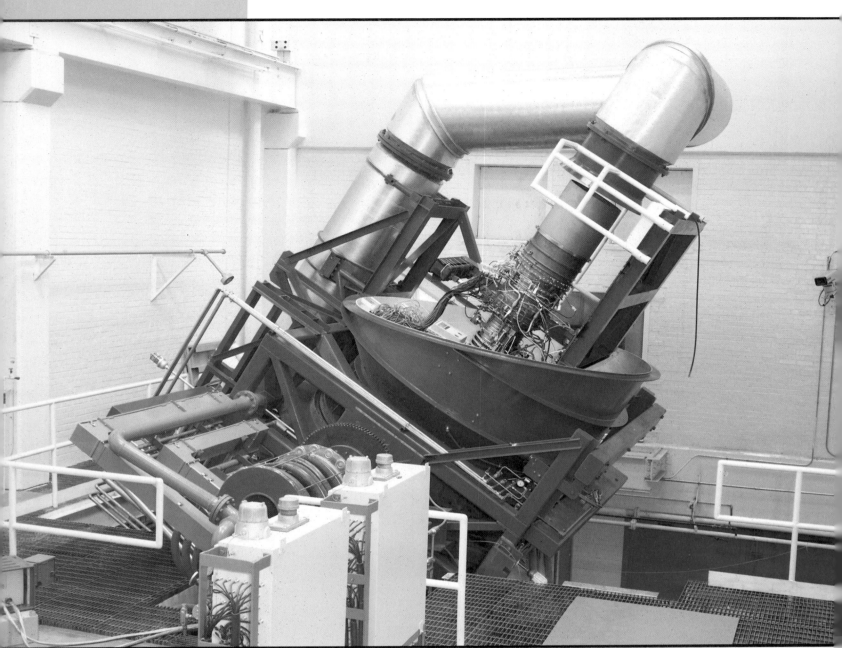

Mirroring the increasingly complex aircraft for whose engines they provide the foundation data, Allison's practical and imaginative test stands have led the industry for decades. The latest version accommodates the T406, and replicates tiltrotor flight attitudes through a 205-degree arc.

Derived from the company's formidably comprehensive experience with the T56/501 engine family, the T406 was first tested in 1988 and has provided the base for military and commercial adaptation. The engine's operation in three test model V-22 Ospreys continues to validate performance expectations.

T406 TECHNICAL FEATURES

PROVEN ADVANCED TECHNOLOGY: LOW RISK, HIGHEST POWER / WEIGHT AVAILABLE

COMPRESSOR
- 90% + AVERAGE STAGE EFFICIENCY
- STEEL BLADE AND VANES
- TOLERANT TO INLET DISTORTION

COMBUSTOR
- SHORT / LIGHT WEIGHT
- SMOKELESS

TURBINE
- TWO STAGE HP
  - SINGLE-CRYSTAL BLADE
  - AIR COOLED
- TWO STAGE LP

444671
VS89-1723

The T406 engine is exemplary. Its development program is on schedule. Engine performance and weight goals have been demonstrated and more than 5,000 test hours have been completed on the engine. The T406 turboprop engine has proven itself—and will be a major factor in the Allison product line for the balance of this decade.

Large Engines Loom Larger

With one division goal being expansion and strengthening in commercial transport engines and high performance military engines, Allison in the mid-1980s joined with Pratt & Whitney to develop and test a PW-Allison propfan propulsion system that was flight tested on a modified McDonnell Douglas MD80, the UHB (Ultra High Bypass) testbed. The 578-DX engine completed its Preliminary Flight Rating Test (PFRT) at Allison in August, 1988.

Testing of the 578-DX, whose basic core is the 570, was conducted in two phases. The first verified component integration and operating characteristics. The second phase achieved two key objectives: verification of the dynamics and structural integrity of the spar/shell propfan blades, and completion of 25 typical demonstrator aircraft flight-mission cycles. With two rows of thin, aerodynamically sweptback propfan blades—manufactured by United Technologies Hamilton Standard—the six-bladed rows rotate in opposite directions.

Continuing its collaborative work with other industry leaders, Allison joined with Pratt & Whitney in December 1986 to develop and test the PW-Allison 578-DX Ultra-High Bypass demonstrator engine. The counter-rotating propfan blades are driven through an Allison gearbox fitted to the basic core—the T406-AD-400 that also powers the Navy's Bell Boeing V-22 Osprey. Prelminary testing was completed in August 1988.

With a 12,000-pound thrust rating, the propfans provide up to 30 percent improvement in cruise SFC over current technology turbofans.

Under the aegis of NASA's Lewis Research Center, America's propfan development team was selected by the National Aeronautic Association to receive the Robert J. Collier Trophy for 1987. According to the NAA announcement, "The NASA/Industry Advanced Turboprop Team has produced a major achievement in aeronautics through the conception, technology development, and flight verification of several advanced turboprop propulsion systems. These systems offer dramatic reductions in fuel usage and operating costs for subsonic transport aircraft. As such, the are expected to power an entire new generation of aircraft for both civil and military use."

In addition to NASA, other participants on the team included GE, Boeing, McDonnell Douglas, Allison, and Pratt & Whitney. Both the P&W-Allison 578-DX and the GE 36 unducted fan (UDF) were flight tested on the McDonnell Douglas UHB aircraft. The intention was for the airframe manufacturer to offer the UHB as a viable commercial transport by the mid-1990s.

Although propfan technology and subsequent flight tests were heralded by the industry, the compelling impetus for development and production of propfan-powered jet transports was fuel economy. When the price of jet fuel dropped significantly late in the 1980s, the propfan's attraction was temporarily dimmed. Major airframe manufacturers McDonnell Douglas, Boeing, and even Airbus (who had toyed with the propfan idea) dropped their plans for propfan-powered aircraft. Boeing disbanded its propfan jet transport team. McDonnell Douglas shifted its development and marketing

As the Turbo-Liner of an earlier day pioneered turboprop technology for America's regional airlines, the 415-mph Saab 2000 promises to set new standards of efficiency and market performance worldwide upon introduction in 1993. The 50-seat airplane will be powered by Allison's 3,650-hp GMA 2100, a derivative of the T406. By spring 1990 140 orders and options had been received, and the prototype was under construction.

emphasis to the MD-90, an advanced, but conventional version of its best-selling MD-80 family of twin-jet aircraft.

Return to the Regionals

Al Novick, director of large engines, succinctly summarizes Allison's historic return to an airline niche it virtually defined:

"A major market breakthrough for Allison's turboprop engine business came with selection in 1989 of the GMA 2100 to power the new Saab 2000 regional propjet. The next-generation version of Saab's extremely successful 340, the 425-mph Saab 2000 is a higher speed, more efficient, twin-engine aircraft with 50 passenger seats for advanced technology utilization by regional carriers."

Based on the highly successful T406, the GMA 2100 combines Allison's 35 years and 130 million flight hours of large turboprop engine experience in 12 different aircraft applications.

Benefiting from technology gained from the NASA high-speed propfan flight test program and the 578-DX propfan flight test demonstration on the McDonnell Douglas UHB, the GMA 2100 also uses FADEC systems integrated with propeller controls to provide for single-lever propulsion system operation.

Testing of the GMA 2100 prototype engine, incorporating new, all-composite, six-bladed Dowty Rotol 6,000-shp-class propellers, began in late 1989. A 60-hour simulated flight endurance test was completed in early 1990. Engine certification is scheduled for early 1992.

In addition to the Saab 2000, scheduled to enter service in 1993, the GMA 2100 has been chosen by Indonesia's Nortrano to power their N-250. Other potential applications for the engine and its derivatives include the military's ASW aircraft and additional regional airliners.

Above: The Saab 2000's slow-turning, six-bladed Dowty propellers are vital to the airplane's quiet efficiency and high performance. Able to take off from a 4,500-ft runway and climb to 20,000 ft in ten minutes—less than most jets—the 2000 can speed 1,000 nautical miles in three hours at 31,000 ft.

Left: Taking further advantage of the proven T406 turboshaft core that lies at the heart of the 578 and the GMA 2100, Allison engineers prepared the state-of-the-art GMA 3007 turbofan engine. The 7,000-lb-thrust powerplant has been chosen to power the Embraer EMB-145 regional airliner.

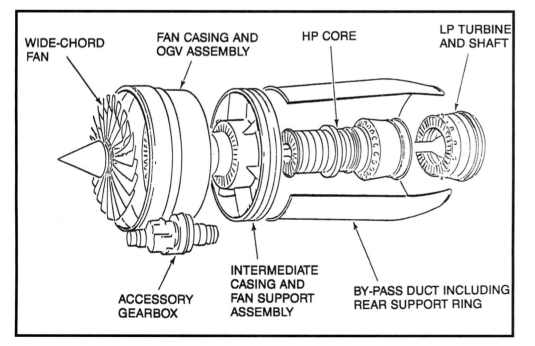

WIDE-CHORD FAN

FAN CASING AND OGV ASSEMBLY

HP CORE

LP TURBINE AND SHAFT

ACCESSORY GEARBOX

INTERMEDIATE CASING AND FAN SUPPORT ASSEMBLY

BY-PASS DUCT INCLUDING REAR SUPPORT RING

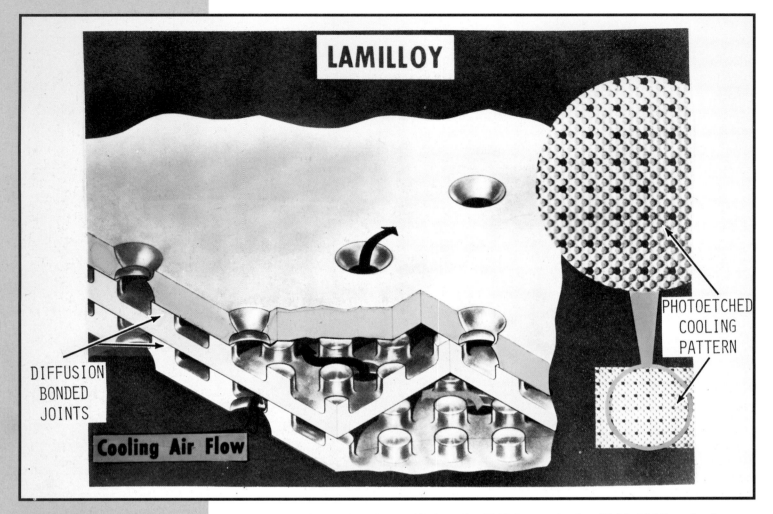

LAMILLOY

DIFFUSION
BONDED
JOINTS

Cooling Air Flow

PHOTOETCHED
COOLING
PATTERN

Among advanced materials developed by Allison engineers is Lamilloy. The concept employs diffusion bonding of photoetched layers of high-strength, light-weight alloys with airflow pathways between layers for air cooling in high temperature applications. Allison materials and structures work has focused on titanium and titanium aluminides reinforced with silicon carbide, as well as Lamilloy.

Another offspring utilizing the T406 core is the GMA 3007 turbofan, a 7000-lb thrust-class engine employing a modern, axial flow configuration, wide-chord fan blades, high efficiency 14-stage axial compressor, single-crystal turbine blades, and FADEC.

The GMA 3007 has been selected to power Embraer's 45-48-seat EMB-145 regional jetliner and has high potential for business aircraft as well as the regional air carrier fleet.

Tomorrow's Developments Today

"The emerging technologies . . . will lead us back to the forefront," believes Mike Hudson, and cutting edge developments continue to flow from the division's research facilities.

One notable example is Allison's patented Lamilloy process. Lamilloy is a porous, engineered material used in hot sections of aircraft gas turbines and other high temperature environments. Fabricated by Allison for producing cooled vanes and turbine rotor blades, Lamilloy combines investment casting, electrochemical etching, and isostatic bonding. The company had fabricated advanced components for high performance fighter engines using the Lamilloy process.

As with many other proprietary processes, the company is actively pursuing other applications for Lamilloy with outside customers. Potential users include rocket manufacturers, producers of combustion systems, and processors of high-temperature chemicals. Director of military programs Eloy Stevens, who joined Allison in 1958, has played a central role in the process of integrating the division's extensive work in new technologies to ensure their maximum utility in every phase of Allison's work.

Under the USAF Advanced Turbine Engine Gas Generator (ATEGG) Program, new technologies are being incorporated into the developmental GMA800 gas generator. ATEGG cores also provide testbeds for fighter engine advances under DOD's Integrated High-Performance Turbine Engine Technology Initiative (IHPTET). With the Navy and Air Force, Allison is refining an advanced fan and low-pressure turbine with the ATEGG core for the two-spool Joint Technology Demonstrator Engine (JTDE).

Successful JTDE testing will position Allison to compete for the next-generation high-performance fighter engine and to reenter the $5 billion-per-year fighter engine market by century-end. ATEGG/JTDE advances will also generate near-term improvements in current products and opportunities to market high-tech components to other engine makers.

Synergy in the GM Family

Valuing technology exchange within the corporation, Allison engineers have pursued dynamic two-way information flow and project participation with other GM units. Ranging from topical problem-solving to major collaborations, joint effort is centered in GM's research, design, and technology groups.

Advanced technology is essential not only for product development, but to assure competitive manufacturing capability as well. Since 1983 Allison has invested millions of dollars to modernize its manufacturing plants, particularly with computer-controlled systems. Such systems allow unprecedented precision for critical operations in making cases, housings, gears, and other components. Automatically controlled vehicles carry case parts from one process station to the next in the Kearney & Trecker Flexible Manufacturing System.

A major asset of the division as a creator of high-performance engines is testing and development of ceramics and other exotic materials. As part of the company's AGT100 (Advanced Gas Turbine) test engine, a number of high-temperature components have been produced using ceramics. Ceramic turbine rotors, for example, have accumulated more than 100 hours of operating time. Ceramics data are being shared in the automotive gas turbine program with Detroit's Advanced Engineering Staff. The development continues to be of interest to planners in GM's automotive divisions.

Notes Wallace, "Ceramics will appear in production reciprocating and turbine engines during the 1990s. Our goal is hot-section components operating at 2,500 degrees Farenheit and above, without expensive cooling, offering up to 30 percent better SFC at half the weight in small turbine engines."

Indianapolis provides support to the Electro-Motive Division on the coal-fueled diesel program, actively participates in the Gear Center of Excellence work on New Departure Hyatt bearings, and plays a major role on the GM Value Management Steering Committee on Value Engineering. The division has been assigned to lead the corporation's work with the Department of Energy on fuel cells, cutting-edge work pursued in collaboration with the

GM Technical Center. Investigation is under way with Delco Electronics on an electronic control system to include vehicle sensors for unmanned automobiles and an expendable gas turbine engine.

Facing the Future

Devotion to excellence thrives all through the Allison Gas Turbine organization. Says Blake Wallace, "The gas turbine business is perhaps the most technically intensive business that I know of, the jet engines themselves intensively designed and developed, using exotic materials under enormous stress, demanding fabrication of complex shapes to exacting tolerances. Every action must focus on the safety of flight even while remaining acutely competitive. There are no easy wins, no easy competition.

"The secret to success is not one thing, but doing the whole range of complex tasks superbly. The business demands an exceptionally skilled and coordinated group of people. I'm most proud, over the past six years, of our people progressing in all these areas simultaneously, continuously improving, building for the future. We've fixed our weaknesses, modernized our factories, and all the while continued to put out first class products.

"We are strongly positioned to meet the challenges we're sure to face in the future. Our strengths come from our expertise and knowledge, from our product line, from our facilities, and, of greatest importance, from our people. The people of Allison have done outstanding, pioneering work in the past. We are continuing that leadership as we move into our next 75 years."

Jim Allison could hardly ask for more.

The division's senior managers gathered in July 1990. From left to right: Mike Hudson, general director of engineering; Joe Byrd, general director of operations; Blake Wallace, general manager; Bill Hutson, general director of finance; Frank Verkamp, general director of product programs; Wilson Burns, director of product assurance and supplier management; and Marvin Recht, general director of personnel and communications.

Allison Engine

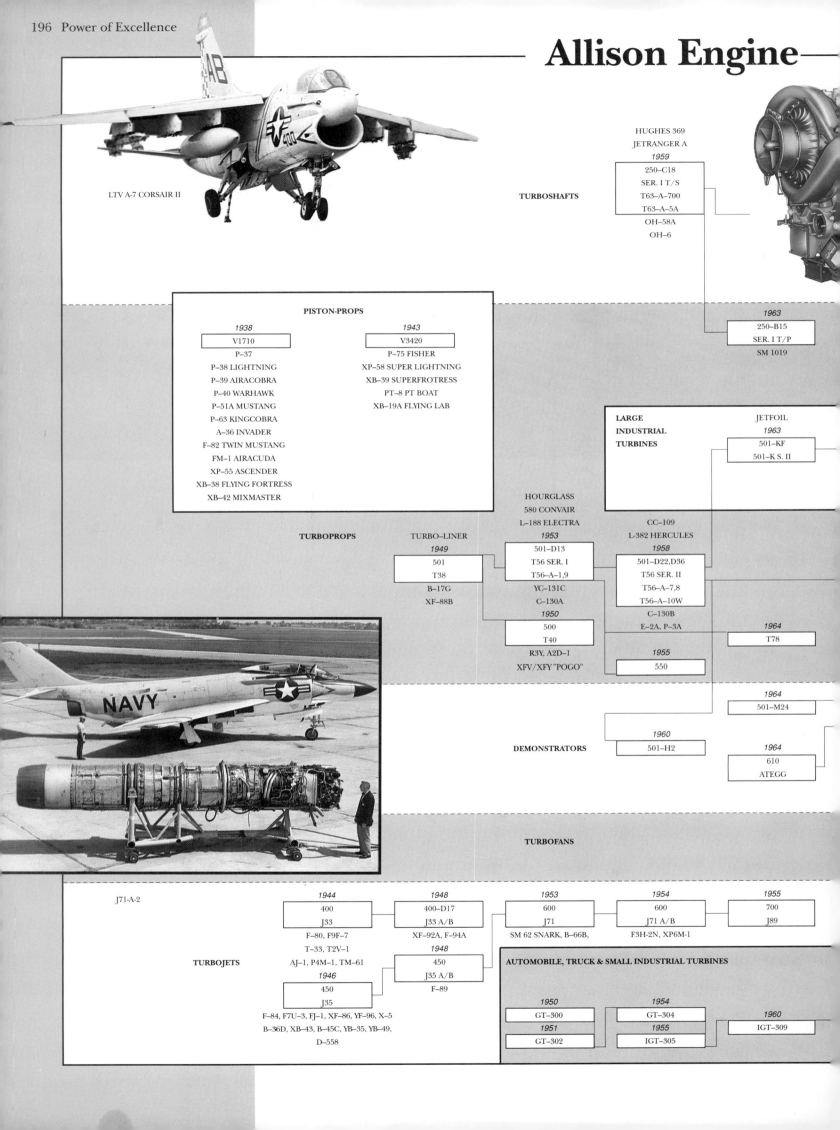

LTV A-7 CORSAIR II

TURBOSHAFTS

HUGHES 369
JETRANGER A
1959

| 250–C18 |
| SER. I T/S |
| T63–A–700 |
| T63–A–5A |
OH–58A
OH–6

1963

| 250–B15 |
| SER. I T/P |
SM 1019

PISTON-PROPS

1938	*1943*
V1710	V3420
P–37	P–75 FISHER
P–38 LIGHTNING	XP–58 SUPER LIGHTNING
P–39 AIRACOBRA	XB–39 SUPERFROTRESS
P–40 WARHAWK	PT–8 PT BOAT
P–51A MUSTANG	XB–19A FLYING LAB
P–63 KINGCOBRA	
A–36 INVADER	
F–82 TWIN MUSTANG	
FM–1 AIRACUDA	
XP–55 ASCENDER	
XB–38 FLYING FORTRESS	
XB–42 MIXMASTER	

LARGE INDUSTRIAL TURBINES

JETFOIL
1963
| 501–KF |
| 501–K S. II |

TURBOPROPS

HOURGLASS
580 CONVAIR
L–188 ELECTRA
1953

TURBO–LINER
1949
| 501 |
| T38 |
B–17G
XF–88B

| 501–D13 |
| T56 SER. I |
| T56–A–1,9 |
YC–131C
C–130A
1950
| 500 |
| T40 |
R3Y, A2D–1
XFV/XFY "POGO"

CC–109
L–382 HERCULES
1958
| 501–D22,D36 |
| T56 SER. II |
| T56–A–7,8 |
| T56–A–10W |
C–130B
E–2A, P–3A
1955
| 550 |

1964
| T78 |

1964
| 501–M24 |

DEMONSTRATORS

1960
| 501–H2 |

1964
| 610 |
ATEGG

TURBOFANS

J71-A-2

1944	*1948*	*1953*	*1954*	*1955*
400	400–D17	600	600	700
J33	J33 A/B	J71	J71 A/B	J89
F–80, F9F–7	XF–92A, F–94A	SM 62 SNARK, B–66B,	F3H-2N, XP6M-1	
T–33, T2V–1	*1948*			
AJ–1, P4M–1, TM–61	450			
1946	J35 A/B			
450	F–89			
J35				

TURBOJETS

F–84, F7U–3, FJ–1, XF–86, YF–96, X–5
B–36D, XB–43, B–45C, YB–35, YB–49,
D–558

AUTOMOBILE, TRUCK & SMALL INDUSTRIAL TURBINES

1950	*1954*	
GT–300	GT–304	*1960*
1951	*1955*	IGT–309
GT–302	IGT–305	

NAVY

Family Tree

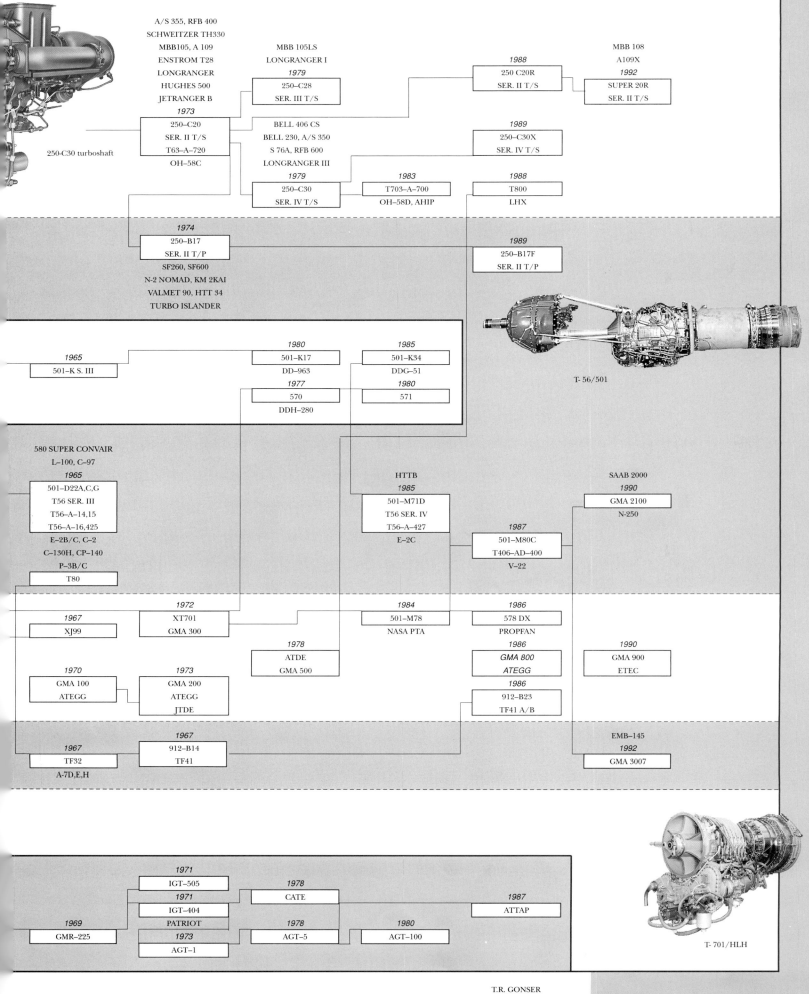

A/S 355, RFB 400
SCHWEITZER TH330

MBB105, A 109
ENSTROM T28
LONGRANGER
HUGHES 500
JETRANGER B

1973

| MBB 105LS |
| LONGRANGER I |
| *1979* |

| 250–C28 |
| SER. III T/S |

| *1988* |
| 250 C20R |
| SER. II T/S |

| MBB 108 |
| A109X |
| *1992* |
| SUPER 20R |
| SER. II T/S |

| 250–C20 |
| SER. II T/S |
| T63–A–720 |
| OH–58C |

250-C30 turboshaft

BELL 406 CS
BELL 230, A/S 350
S 76A, RFB 600
LONGRANGER III

| *1979* |
| 250–C30 |
| SER. IV T/S |

| *1983* |
| T703–A–700 |
| OH–58D, AHIP |

| *1989* |
| 250–C30X |
| SER. IV T/S |

| *1988* |
| T800 |
| LHX |

| *1974* |
| 250–B17 |
| SER. II T/P |

SF260, SF600
N-2 NOMAD, KM 2KAI
VALMET 90, HTT 34
TURBO ISLANDER

| *1989* |
| 250–B17F |
| SER. II T/P |

T- 56/501

| *1965* |
| 501–K S. III |

| *1980* |
| 501–K17 |
| DD–963 |

| *1985* |
| 501–K34 |
| DDG–51 |

| *1977* |
| 570 |
| DDH–280 |

| *1980* |
| 571 |

580 SUPER CONVAIR
L–100, C–97

| *1965* |
| 501–D22A,C,G |
| T56 SER. III |
| T56–A–14,15 |
| T56–A–16,425 |
| E–2B/C, C–2 |
| C–130H, CP–140 |
| P–3B/C |

| T80 |

HTTB

| *1985* |
| 501–M71D |
| T56 SER. IV |
| T56–A–427 |
| E–2C |

| *1987* |
| 501–M80C |
| T406–AD–400 |
| V–22 |

SAAB 2000

| *1990* |
| GMA 2100 |
| N-250 |

| *1967* |
| XJ99 |

| *1972* |
| XT701 |
| GMA 300 |

| *1984* |
| 501–M78 |
| NASA PTA |

| *1986* |
| 578 DX |
| PROPFAN |

| *1978* |
| ATDE |
| GMA 500 |

| *1986* |
| *GMA 800* |
| *ATEGG* |

| *1986* |
| 912–B23 |
| TF41 A/B |

| *1990* |
| GMA 900 |
| ETEC |

| *1970* |
| GMA 100 |
| ATEGG |

| *1973* |
| GMA 200 |
| ATEGG |
| JTDE |

| *1967* |
| TF32 |
| A-7D,E,H |

| *1967* |
| 912–B14 |
| TF41 |

EMB–145

| *1992* |
| GMA 3007 |

| *1971* |
| IGT–505 |

| *1971* |
| IGT–404 |
| PATRIOT |

| *1973* |
| AGT–1 |

| *1978* |
| CATE |

| *1978* |
| AGT–5 |

| *1980* |
| AGT–100 |

| *1987* |
| ATTAP |

| *1969* |
| GMR–225 |

T- 701/HLH

T.R. GONSER
23 MAY 90

DATE	EVENT	DATE	EVENT
September 14, 1915	Allison founded as the Indianapolis Speedway Team Company, James A. Allison, President.	June 25, 1958	Allison receives contract for T63/Model 250 engine development.
March 26, 1929	Allison Engineering Company bought by General Motors.	November 14, 1960	Allison begins work on Minuteman second-stage rocket engine cases.
March 12, 1932	First V1710 engine delivered to the U.S. Navy.	March 26, 1963	Allison receives contract to build components for Apollo space program.
December 7, 1941	Pearl Harbor and beginning of U.S. efforts in WWII. V1710 orders to 1,100 engines/month.	June 5, 1963	Allison announces Model 501 industrial engine program.
June 1942	Construction of Plant 5 begins. (It's now our major production facility.)	January 3, 1964	Allison awarded contract for production of T56 engines for the P3 Orion aircraft.
August 1943	V1710 engine production reaches a peak of 2,105 engines/month.	April 24, 1964	Allison awarded the contract to build propellant tanks for the lunar excursion module of NASA's Apollo spacecraft.
June 1944	Allison wins the contract to build J33 jet engines.	April 27, 1966	Allison and Rolls-Royce are selected for a joint program to develop a new turbojet lift engine called the XJ99. (This begins our association with Rolls-Royce which still continues today.)
October 1944	Allison wins the contract to build J31 jet engines.		
June 1946	Production is started on marine gears for Detroit Diesel Division, GM, thus entering us in the transmission business for the first time.		
		January 6, 1967	Allison is awarded the contract for development of the TF41 to power the A-7 aircraft. The engine is a collaborative effort between Rolls-Royce and Allison.
June 20, 1946	Allison signs contract for development of T40 turboprop engine.		
September 12, 1947	Allison takes over complete engineering and production responsibility for J35 jet engines.	August 17, 1968	Two new 400-shp Model 250 engines, the 250-C20 turboshaft and 250-B17C turboprop, are announced.
April 1949	Allison begins design of high-thrust J71 engine.	July 20, 1969	Apollo 11 lands on the moon. Allison technology has been a part of the mission.
November 21, 1951	Construction of Plant 8 begins. (It's now our administration, research, and development center.)	September 1, 1970	Allison merged with Detroit Diesel to form Detroit Diesel Allison Division.
September 15, 1942	Aeroproducts (propeller company) becomes consolidated with Allison.	August 25, 1971	Allison GT404 enters limited production for highway, marine, and industrial applications.
November 1953	First T56 built in production.	February 1973	Allison receives contract to design and develop XT-701 turboshaft engine to power the U.S. Army's Heavy Lift Helicopter.
January 10, 1955	First T56 delivered for the C-130 aircraft.		

Allison Gas Turbine

DATE	EVENT	DATE	EVENT
May 1973	Allison 501-K turbine selected to power Boeing's new Jetfoil, the first marine application for the engine.	July 19, 1985	Allison/Garrett team selected by the Army to develop a T800 engine to power the LHX light attack helicopter.
September 1973	New 420-shp engine, the Model 250-C20B, is added to the product line.	December 24, 1985	Allison engine selected to power the V-22 tilt-rotor aircraft. (Engine was later designated the T406.)
October 1974	New Model 250-C28 makes first run.	June 4, 1986	NASA successfully tests propfan aircraft powered by Allison gas turbine engine in the Propfan Test Assessment program.
January 1975	New 650-shp engine, the Model 250-C30, is added to the product line.		
February 1977	The Model 570, a 7,000 shaft horsepower industrial and marine gas turbine, is announced.	February 23, 1987	Allison and Pratt & Whitney form PW-Allison Engines to test counter-rotating 578-DX propfan.
March 1, 1983	F. Blake Wallace named General Director, Gas Turbine Research, Engineering, and Sales.	September 4, 1988	Allison announces it has signed a licensing agreement to market and manufacture low-cost missile engines designed by Noel Penny Turbine Limited of Coventry, England.
September 1, 1983	Gas turbine operations separated from Detroit Diesel Allison as Allison Gas Turbine. F. Blake Wallace appointed General Director.		
April 23, 1984	Allison elevated to divisional status. Wallace named General Manager.	October 17, 1988	Allison/Garrett LHTEC T800 engines fly for the first time, in an Agusta A129 aircraft.
August 8, 1984	Allison and Garrett form the Light Helicopter Turbine Engine Company, LHTEC, to compete for design and development of the engine that will power the Army's forthcoming LHX light attack helicopter.	October 28, 1988	The LHTEC team of Allison and Garrett is awarded the contract to complete development of their T800 powerplant for the Army's LHX light attack helicopter.
October 1984	T56-A-427, the fourth generation of T56 engines, selected to power the newest E-2C aircraft.	March 20, 1989	V-22 tiltrotor aircraft flies for the first time on Allison T406 engines.
October 1984	Allison Energy Systems created to market cogeneration systems powered by Allison engines.	April 13, 1989	First flight of the McDonnell Douglas MD-80 testbed aircraft with PW-Allison 578-DX propfan engine.
January 17, 1985	Allison announces Model 250-C20R engine flat-rated at 450 horsepower.	July 11, 1989	Allison's GMA 2100 turboprop engine selected by Saab-Scania for their high-speed, 50-seat SAAB 2000 regional airliner.
		March 23, 1990	Allison's GMA 3007 turbofan engine selected by Embraer for their 45-seat regional fanjet liner, the EMB-145.

Allison Firsts

April 1938	V1710-E makes first flight in Bell XP-39 Airacuda.
October 1938	Curtiss XP-40 Warhawk makes first flight with V1710-C15.
January 1939	Left and right-hand rotation V1710 engines make first flight in Lockheed XP-38 Lightning.
February 1939	XP-38 breaks transcontinental speed record.
April 1943	Lockheed P-38L sets U.S. altitude record of 44,940 ft.
February 1945	Allison ships first J33 jet engine.
May 1945	Allison builds first J31 jet engine (total of 22 built).
January 1946	USAAF Col. W.H. Councill pilots Allison J33-powered P-80 to world record from Long Beach, CA, to NYC: 2,453.807 miles in 4 hrs, 13 min., 26 seconds.
July 1946	First jet airmail letter delivered to President Truman in Washington, D.C., by Allison-powered F-80 from Schenectady, NY, in 49-minute flight.
September 1946	Allison J33 jet engine first to pass new Army and Navy 100-hour type test.
January 1947	Allison introduces production of jet engines with water/alcohol augmentation in J33-A-21.
April 1947	J33-A-21 is first jet to pass USAF 150-hour qualification.
May 1948	Allison J33-A-21 given CAA Type Certificate — the first jet engine ever approved for U.S. commercial use.
January 1949	First flight of the first jet-powered missile in this country is made by Martin Matador with Allison J33-A-14.
April 1949	First flight of Allison turboprop engine is made with Allison T38, the fifth engine on Boeing B-17 at Weir Cook Municipal Airport, Indianapolis.
August 1949	Allison J33-A-33 makes first afterburner flight, in F-94.
September 1949	First production afterburner jet, an Allison J33-A-33.
April 1950	Allison turboprop engines make first flight independent of other engines, in Convair XP5Y.
May 1950	J33-A-33, first afterburner engine, passes 150-hour qualification test.
June 1950	Allison-powered jet fighters (Lockheed F-80s) enter combat in Korea.
November 1950	First flight of Chance Vought Regulus (Navy missile) with Allison J33-A-18.
December 1950	Turbo-Liner first flies, at Lindbergh Field, San Diego.
August 1951	Allison J35 becomes first engine to operate 1,000 hours before overhaul. Accomplished by J35-A-13D at Hamilton Air Force Base.
November 1953	First T56 turboprop engine built in production.
August 1954	Allison J33-A-35 becomes first turbojet engine to complete 1,400 hours operation without major overhaul, at Tyndall AFB.
September 1954	Convair XFY-1 completes first flight in vertical position at Brown Field.
January 1955	First production T56 engine shipped for C-130.
January 1956	Production completed on 100,000 aircraft engines.
November 1958	First delivery of an Electra by Lockheed to an airline: Eastern.
January 1959	First scheduled commercial Electra flight: Eastern Air Lines, Flt. 602 from Miami to Idlewild, New York.
February 1959	First Allison-designed vectoring nozzle for Minuteman rocket case passes initial test.

April 1959	Allison T63 turboshaft engine makes first run.
January 1960	First complete Convair 580 conversion flies.
April 1960	FAA certifies 580 for commercial service.
November 1960	Allison announces liquid metal fuel cell.
January 1961	First flight of Bell UH-13R, with T63 turboshaft.
April 1962	Allison ships first T63-A-5 engine.
December 1962	FAA and Army approve T63 for commercial, military use.
May 1964	Allison builds first full-scale engine with air-cooled turbine blades and vanes.
September 1964	Allison builds aerospace industry's largest pressure tank, for USAF Titan III-C missile.
March 1965	T78 regenerative engine for Navy runs one month early.
July 1966	Allison is first Indiana firm to win USAF award for outstanding Zero Defects Program.
April 1967	T56 passes record 5,000-hour simulated endurance test.
October 1967	Allison flies Model 250-E3, first regenerative engine to provide sole-source power for an aircraft.
October 1968	Four Allison propellant tanks help Apollo 7 complete historic 11-day manned space flight.
February 1969	Allison/Rolls XJ99 advanced lift engine completes first runs in U.K. and U.S.
July 1969	Allison descent-stage propellant tanks help Apollo 11 astronauts make first human lunar landing.
January 1971	First 250-B17 turboprops shipped to Government Aircraft Factory, Australia, for N-2 aircraft.
May 1972	First gyro-tested engine, 3.5 radians per second.
March 1975	Highest compressor airflow per frontal area.
July 1977	PHI, Inc. is first civil operator to log one million hours on Model 250 engines.
September 1978	Highest pressure ratio, single-stage centrifugal compressor.
April 1981	First cast titanium fan stage.
June 1982	Highest pressure ratio single-spool compressor, 21:1.
August 1987	First fabricated metal matrix composite spacer successfully spin tested.
June 1989	World's first dual-pulse induction hardening system.
June 1989	First U.S. production-size plasma carburizing heat treating system.
August 1989	First Lamilloy engine nozzle liner, ATF.
July 1990	Record-breaking ultra-high temperature turbine successfully tested.

Product Support

As Allison prepares to re-enter the airline business with the GMA 2100—even while advancing in the industry's most demanding defense projects—perhaps none of its professional team is more competent and eager than the men and women responsible for Product Support.

The Tradition

The Product Support team honors is steeped in traditions that began with reduction gears and bearings before the First World War. These powerful loyalties and pride were tempered by the trials of WWII and further nurtured as Allison became a jet engine leader in the postwar era. Then, the high-volume civil and military market support needs created by the T56/501 and T63/250 engine families and the TF41 demanded still more efficient and responsive support systems.

From trend-setting engine exchange programs and battlefield maintenance to the relentless pressure of air carrier schedules in the nation's busiest markets, Allison mastered every requisite skill, from writing easy-to-use manuals to monitoring operators' cockpit procedures.

Cutting Edge Service

The group now has access to sophisticated computer technology and management systems that put the division at the industry's leading edge. Especially helpful is the ongoing two-way exchange of improvements generated between maturing military projects and commercial programs. For automation of logistics analysis, publications, training, service parts, and software design, for instance, Allison is in the vanguard of GM's efforts in the Computer Aided Acquisition and Logistic Support (CALS) Initiative of the Defense Department.

For civil as well as military programs, application of Integrated Logistic Support (ILS) principles emphasizes a disciplined, unified approach to management and technical activities in all phases of hardware systems design and development. The system ensures that products are maintainable, reliable, supportable, and cost effective. Increasing emphasis is placed on concurrent engineering to design in attributes that enhance supportability. ILS integrates logistic elements such as maintenance planning, manpower, tools, facilities, engine monitoring systems (EMS), and spare parts for complete systems support.

At Indianapolis headquarters and in the field, the most modern test and communications facilities provide product support staff with speedy and comprehensive response ability for all phases of each engine program. As new programs come on line, headquarters engineers direct operational support and overhaul and repair of production engines to ensure early resolution of service-revealed deficiencies. They coordinate the cooperation of other division groups, from engineering to publications and training, to resolve early problems and to take corrective action.

Simultaneously, on-site representatives become the division's direct link with the customer to resolve field problems promptly, to see that training is adapted to prevent problem recurrence, and to detect performance patterns that may signal future problems. The GMA 2100 Product Support Team, for example, began three years in advance to plan strategic regional offices and parts depots for optimum product and information flow and coordination of project management.

As engines move into certification, production, and delivery, the product support manager is ready to respond to both engineering and program management needs. As delivery commences, field reps shift focus to customer-generated needs through the manager of field support activities to assure optimum orientation and manpower use.

Allison Management

1915-1928	James A. Allison, President Speedway Team Company 1915 Allison Experimental Company 1917 Allison Engineering Company 1920
1929	Edward V. Rickenbacker, President Allison Engineering Company, under Fisher & Company
1929-1936	Norman H. Gilman, President and General Manager Allison Engineering Company 1929 Allison Division of General Motors Corporation 1934
1937-1940	Otto T. "Pop" Kreusser, General Manager Allison Division
1940-1942	Fred C. Kroeger, General Manager Allison Division
1942-1943	Cy Osborn, General Manager Allison Division Vice President, General Motors Corporation
1943-1960	Edward B. Newill, General Manager Allison Division Vice President, General Motors Corporation
1960-1965	Harold H. Dice, General Manager Allison Division Vice President, General Motors Corporation
1965-1967	James E. Knott, Manager of Indianapolis Plants Allison Division
1967-1970	Reuben R. Jensen, General Manager Allison Division Vice President, General Motors Corporation
1970-1978	James E. Knott, General Manager Detroit Diesel Allison Division Vice President, General Motors Corporation
1978-1981	Donald J. Atwood, General Manager Detroit Diesel Allison Division Vice President, General Motors Corporation
1981-1982	Harold L. Smith, General Manager Detroit Diesel Allison Division Vice President, General Motors Corporation
1982-1988	Ludvik F. Koci, General Manager Detroit Diesel Allison Division Vice President, General Motors Corporation
1983-Present	F. Blake Wallace, General Manager Allison Gas Turbine Division Vice President, General Motors Corporation

Allison Gas Turbine Division
Distributors

AEROMARITIME MEDITERRANEAN

Aeromaritime Mediterranean
Washington, D.C., USA

Aviall
Dallas, Texas, USA

Airwork Corporation
Millville, New Jersey, USA

Centrax LTD
Devon, England, UK

Detroit Engine and Turbine Company
Adelaide, South Australia

Elicotteri Meridionali
Frosinone, Italy

Equipamientos
Rio de Janeiro, Brazil

H & S Aviation
Hampshire, England, UK

Hawker Pacific
New South Wales, Australia

National Airmotive Corporation
Oakland, California, USA

National Airways Corporation
Johannesburg, South Africa

Standard Aero
Winnipeg, Manitoba, Canada

Stewart & Stevenson
Houston, Texas, USA

Tominaga & Company LTD.
Tokyo, Japan

U.S. Turbine
Maineville, Ohio, USA

Allison Engine Production

Engine Model	Quantity
Liberty	Several hundred original units; c. 2,500 rebuilt
Allison Twelve Marine	12
Dirigible	6
V1710	70,033
J33	15,525
J35	14,169
J71	1,707
TF41	1,414
T56, including 501D	14,849*
501K Industrial	1,353*
570 and 571 Industrial	108*
404	143
T63	5,768*
250	23,043
T406	21*

Projected through calendar 1990.

The Future Is Now

Large Engines

T56/501D Series III

Weight, 1,835 lbs
Pressure ratio, 9.5:1
Air Flow (lbs/sec), 32.35
Compressor stages, 14
Turbine stages, 4
Allowable bleed air, 8%
Engine speed, 13,820 rpm
Reduction gear ratio, 13.54:1
Maximum rate gas temperature, 1,970°F

   The world's most proven turboprop engine: since 1954, 14,000 orders steadily reaffirm unmatched value. Continuous refinement has marked three major iterations in T56 design. With advancing economy, performance, and reliability, each series has retained its predecessor's installation envelope. Among Series III improvements: changed bearing material and design for greater load capacity and pinion assembly reliability; main drive gear faces coated for vibration dampening; improved turbine interstage sealing with rotating knife seals mating to honeycomb static components; unique blade and vane coating to decrease hot gas corrosion.

T56/501D Series IV

Dry weight, 1,934 lb.
Length, 146"
Height, 39"
RPM, 14,239
Reduction gear ratio, 13.96:1
Pressure ratio, 14.1:1
SFC, takeoff, 0.469 lb/hr/shp, 0.444 lb/hr/eshp.
   Air blast fuel nozzles for virtual smoke-free operation • Compressor components with knife-edge seals • Corrosion-resistant vane and blade coating on first and second turbine stages • Digital electronic control • Engine monitoring system (EMS) provide performance tracking and maintenance diagnostic aid • Honeycomb turbine blade track improve efficiency • Single-crystal blades in turbine second stage • Turbine thermocouples between the second and third stages for long life.

T406-AD-400
Free-power turbine turboshaft
Length, 77.08"
Width, 28.80"
Height, 34.90"
Dry Weight, 971 lbs.
Output shaft speed, 15,000 rpm
Power: Takeoff, sea level, 103°: 6,150 shp
        Cruise, 20,000 ft; Mach 0.55, 3,584 shp
Maximum turbine temperature, 2,200°F
All-attitude operation, pitch to 110° up and 90° down, roll +55°

All-axial, high-efficiency turbo components • Annular combustor • Digital electronic fuel control • Dual independent FADEC systems • Electric system: 28V DC, 5 amp • Engine casings designed for blade containment • Engine Monitoring System (EMS) for on-condition maintenance, rapid fault isolation, engine health monitoring usage and tracking • 14-stage axial flow compressor, six variable stator stages • HP turbine, two-stage, air-cooled; LP turbine, two stage, non-air-cooled • Ignition: capacitor discharge tube • Modular construction • More than seven shp per pound of weight • Only four main rotor bearings • Positive pump scavenging • Reduced exposed area of lubrication/fuel systems • Splined compressor disks reduce ballistic vulnerability • Suction fuel system reduces fire risk.

GMA 2100
Length, 107.64"
Height, 45.34"
Certification at 4,550 shp

Compressor above 90% average stage efficiency; steel blades and vanes; high distortion and FOD tolerance • Cored oil passages • Gearbox: 30,000 hrs reliability; lightweight; accommodates modular propeller controls and accessories; line-replaceable accessory gearcase • Multiple borescope ports • Prop diagnostics with engine FADEC • Replaceable prop seals • Smokeless combustor • Turbine: two-stage HP, single-crystal, air-cooled; two-stage LP.

GMA3007
Length, 106.5"
Width, 43.5"
Height, 51.9"
Uninstalled Performance:

	SLS, ISA Max Takeoff	35K, 0.7, ISA Max Cruise
Fn (lbf)	7,160	1,830
Inlet flow (lbm/sec)	251	289
BPR	5	5
OPR	18.6	22.7
RIT (°F)	1,970	1,880

Blade and vane spacing for low noise • Control and sensor redundancy • Direct drive • Full authority digital electronic control (FADEC), with fault identification and accommodation • Family commonality with T406 and GMA 2100 • Inherent growth margin • Large, well-placed access panels • Low operating temperatures • Maximum FOD resistance • Multiple borescope inspection ports • Quick-disconnect accessories • Replaceable, rugged wide-chord fan blades • Single-stage fan • Smokeless with low emissions.

Small Engines

250-C20R
Weight, 173 lbs.
Power/weight ratio (T.O. thermodynamic) 2.86:1
Airflow (T.O.), 3.82 lbs/sec
Pressure ratio (T.O.), 7.9
Design speeds at 100% rpm: Power output shaft, 6,016 rpm;
Gas producer rotor, 50,970 rpm; Power turbine rotor, 33,290 rpm
Sea level static performance: normal cruise, 380 shp; five minute takeoff, 30-minute power, and maximum continuous, all 450 shp.

Average operating fuel usage 4% less than a C20B doing the same work; at 420 shp, uses 7% less fuel • *Gearbox bearing improvements offer 60% added life* • *Hot day performance better than B throughout most of normal operating envelope: at 80°F, has a 14% power advantage at takeoff and 12% at cruise; at higher altitudes, the R has a 20% advantage over the B* • *Larger blade and vane chord width, airfoil thickness, and case coating increase service life* • *More rugged stainless steel compressor case with sprayed aluminum flow path for fewer repairs* • *New blade coatings increase corrosion resistance* • *Redesigned bearings and improved materials for 60% longer bearing life.*

250-C30S

Weight, 249 lbs.
Power/weight ratio (T.O), 2.61
Airflow (T.O) 5.6 lb/sec
Pressure ratio (T.O) 8.6
Design speeds at 100% rpm: power output shaft, 6,016 rpm; gas producer, 51,000 rpm; power turbine, 30,650 rpm
Performance shp: 2.5-minute, 700; takeoff, 30-minute, and maximum continuous, 650 each; normal cruise, 557.

Better cruise performance • *Cooler operating temperatures* • *Lower fuel consumption* • *More takeoff power.*

T800

Length, 33.3"
Width, 21.5"
Height, 25.8"
Base weight, 300 lbs.
Power, 1,300+ shp class
SFC, .46 class (lb/hp/hr)
Output speed, 23,000 rpm (6,000-6,600 rpm, with reduction gearbox)

Adaptive FADEC • *All electrical or optical control links to aircraft* • *Compatible with all aircraft start systems* • *Corrosion-resistant materials* • *Engine surge margin and control system for stable operation* • *Gearbox and accessories located for maximum ballistic protection* • *Growth over 50% in frame size* • *Inlet particle separation capability above 97%* • *Minimized external envelope* • *Multi-fuel capability* • *Multiple mounting arrangements* • *No complex geometry* • *Operation from 45° nose down to 105° nose up* • *Power/weight ratio, over 4.5:1 at maximum rating* • *Reduced parts count* • *Self-contained engine electrical system* • *Simplified battlefield repairs* • *6,000-hour design life* • *Suction fuel system for fire safety.*

Industrial Engines

501K

5,000 hp class
Weight, 1,270 lbs.
Applications: compressors and pumps for pipelines; gas gathering apparatus; secondary petroleum recovery devices; emergency electric sets for critical communications such as computer systems for hospital, police, fire, and other emergency operations.

First stage turbine blade and vane coating of diffusion-bonded aluminum (AEO) for improved durability • *Interior liner wall thermal barrier coating increases liner life and combustion efficiency* • *Low emission liner, developed for the Navy, to eliminate smoke and extend turbine life* • *Modular design for easy maintenance and service* • *Quad entry fuel nozzle for gaseous or liquid fuel with auto switch-over retaining water injection capability* • *Split outer combustion case for field exchange with minimal expense and downtime* • *Water injection reduces NOX emissions up to 70% while boosting hp up to 8.5% without increasing operating temperature.*

570K and 571K

8,000-hp class
Weight, 1,840 lbs

Air-cooled turbine blades and vanes for higher gas temperatures and efficiency without reducing engine life • *Fuel injection nozzles accommodate either gaseous or liquid fuel as well as injected water* • *Labyrinth seals, virtually wear-free, with honeycomb, debris-free surface for longer bearing life, less leakage* • *Modular construction reduces maintenance downtime* • *Radial air inlet option for installations where space precludes straight-in airflow.*

General Index

See also, **Index to Aircraft and Index to Engines**

Italics denote illustrations.

Index to Aircraft

Index to Engines

Cover and Endpapers

The cover and endpapers are original paintings executed for the Allison 75th Anniversary by distinguished American illustrator James Dietz. The cover reflects the division's contemporary era, highlighting the engines that are the standard of their types, the turboprop T56/501 and the turboshaft and turboprop T63/250. Represented, too, are the c. 1970s turbofan TF41 and the GMA 2100 and GMA 3007 next-generation turboprops that will power tomorrow's swift, efficient, quiet regional airliners.

The front endpaper recalls founder Jim Allison and his company's early job shop days of Indy racing, Liberty engines, and the Gilman bearing. The back endpaper evokes the company's contribution to Allied victory in WWII—the superb powerplant of Warhawks and Airacobras, Lightnings and Mustangs—the V1710 engine. Included are early Allison entries into the turbojet business—the J33s and J35s for Shooting Stars, Scorpions, and Thunderjets—that set world standards for jet engine performance and reliability.

About the Authors

Paul Sonnenburg, born in Duluth, Minnesota, and educated at the University of Southern California, began writing about aero engines as a maintenance planner with Northeast Airlines in Washington, D.C., 30 years ago. After a tour with the U.S. Army in Alaska, Paul served in administration and public relations with TWA and Air-India in New York City. He worked with the Los Angeles Community Colleges in establishing their overseas education programs for the armed services. A director of the Los Angeles City College Foundation, for eight years Paul was a division manager and consultant for an international publisher of regional history books.

William Schoneberger, author and co-author of three aviation and aerospace industry history books, has reported, participated in, and chronicled three decades of aviation and aerospace milestone events. Since 1979 he has operated William A. Schoneberger Communications, specializing in public relations counsel, representation, and writing. A Cincinnati native, Bill graduated from the University of South Carolina and also attended Miami University (Ohio) and the University of Cincinnati. Presently preparing a biography of John K. Northrop, Bill is contributing editor for a major airline trade magazine, president of the Aero Club of Southern California, and Western regional director of the Aviation/Space Writers Association. Bill Schoneberger's book credits include 1980's award-winning *Seven Decades of Progress*, a history of the General Electric Corporation's gas turbine operations; and the 1986 *Out of Thin Air*, a history of the Garrett Corporation (with Robert R.H. Scholl).

Bill Schoneberger and Paul Sonnenburg collaborated in 1984 on *California Wings: A History of Aviation in the Golden State*, warmly received in the industry and notable as the first single volume narration of all the major facets of the state's remarkably diverse contributions to aviation and aerospace achievement.

About the Artist

San Francisco native Jim Dietz began his career after graduation from Art Center College of Design in Los Angeles in 1969. His gold medal-winning work has appeared in leading magazines, on book jackets, and in Hollywood films. In addition to gallery showings across the nation, Jim has been honored by exhibitions at the Smithsonian Institution and the San Diego Aero Space Museum. He earned best of show honors at the Experimental Aviation Association Art Show for three of the past four years. Jim Dietz lives in Seattle, Washington.

About the Designer

Book designer Robaire Ream, Colorado-born, Paris-raised, and educated in France and Southern California, has designed more than 150 hardcover books and softcover publications. An accomplished artist in several media, notably pencil and pen-and-ink, Robaire is an assistant art director at the Los Angeles book publishing house, Windsor Publications. From computer textbooks to academic anthologies, Robaire's work is noted for textual clarity and bold use of photographic imagery.

About the Photos

Unless otherwise attributed, photographs and drawings come from the Allison Gas Turbine and Allison Transmission division archives in Indianapolis. The Allison Engine Family Tree was prepared by Chris Murray.